MW00654743

God's Design: Heaven & Earth

MASTER BOOKS CURRICULUM

Master Books Creative Team:
Authors: Richard and Debbie Lawrence
Editor: Craig Froman
Design: Terry White
Cover Design: Diana Bogardus
Copy Editors: Judy Lewis, Willow Meek
Curriculum Review: Kristin Pratt, Laura Welch, Diana Bogardus

First printing: May 2018
Fifth printing: May 2021

Master Books®, P.O. Box 726, Green Forest, AR 72638

Master Books® is a division of the New Leaf Publishing Group, Inc.

ISBN: 978-1-68344-130-4

ISBN: 978-1-61458-654-8 (digital)

Scripture taken from the New King James Version. Copyright © 1982 by Thomas Nelson, Inc. Used by permission. All rights reserved.

Printed in the United States of America

Please visit our website for other great titles:
www.masterbooks.com

The God's Design Science series is based on a biblical worldview and reveals how science supports the biblical account of creation. **Richard and Debbie Lawrence**, authors of the series, have a long history of enjoying science. They have both worked as electrical engineers and now Debbie teaches chemistry and physics at a homeschool co-op. While homeschooling their children for 16 years, there was almost always a science experiment going on in the kitchen. Today that tradition is being continued with the next generation as the grandkids enjoy Grandma Science Day once a week.

Your reputation as a publisher is stellar. It is a blessing knowing anything I purchase from you is going to be worth every penny!

—Cheri ★ ★ ★ ★ ★

Last year we found Master Books and it has made a HUGE difference.

—Melanie ★ ★ ★ ★ ★

We love Master Books and the way it's set up for easy planning!

—Melissa ★ ★ ★ ★ ★

You have done a great job. MASTER BOOKS ROCKS!

—Stephanie ★ ★ ★ ★ ★

Physically high-quality, Biblically faithful, and well-written.

—Danika ★ ★ ★ ★ ★

Best books ever. Their illustrations are captivating and content amazing!

—Kathy ★ ★ ★ ★ ★

Affordable
Flexible
Faith Building

Table of Contents

Publisher's note: Internet links on the Works Cited pages in the appendices were valid at the time of the first printing. Those on sites other than masterbooks.com that we do not maintain may be changed or deleted by that particular company. We apologize for any inconvenience this may cause.

Activities warning: The publisher and authors have made every reasonable effort to ensure that the activities recommended in this book are safe when performed as instructed but assume no responsibility for any damage caused or sustained while conducting the experiments and activities. It is the parents', guardians', and/or teachers' responsibility to supervise all recommended activities. Please protect surfaces when using food coloring, paint, and other materials that may stain surfaces.

Welcome to GOD'S DESIGN®

HEAVEN & EARTH

God's Design for Heaven and Earth is a series that has been designed for use in teaching earth science to elementary and middle school students. It is divided into three units: *Our Universe*, *Our Planet Earth*, and *Our Weather and Water*. Each unit has 35 lessons including a final project that ties all of the lessons together.

In addition to the lessons, special features in each unit include biographical information on interesting people as well as fun facts to make the subject more fun.

Although this is a complete curriculum, the information included here is just a beginning, so please feel free to add to each lesson as you see fit. A resource guide is included in the appendices to help you find additional information and resources. A list of supplies needed is included at the beginning of each lesson, while a master list of all supplies needed for the entire series can be found in the appendices.

Answer keys for all review questions, worksheets, quizzes, and the final exams are included. If you wish to get through *God's Design: Heaven & Earth* in one year, plan on covering approximately three to four lessons per week. The time required for each lesson varies depending on how much additional information you include, but plan on about 40 to 45 minutes. A helpful daily schedule starts on page 15. Quizzes may be given at the conclusion of each unit, and a final exam may be given at the completion of each section. If you wish to cover the material in more depth, you may add additional information and take a longer period of time to cover all the material, or you could choose to do only one or two of the sections as a unit study.

Why Teach Earth Science?

It is not uncommon to question the need to teach children hands-on science in elementary or middle school. We could argue that the knowledge gained in science will be needed later in life in order for children to be more productive and well-rounded adults. We could argue that teaching children science also teaches them logical and inductive thinking and reasoning skills, which are tools they will need to be more successful. We could argue that science is a necessity in this technological world in which we live. While all of these arguments are true, not one of them is the main reason that we should teach our children science. The most important reason to teach science in elementary school is to give children an understanding that God is our Creator, and the Bible can be trusted. Teaching science from a creation perspective is one of the best ways to reinforce our children's faith in God and to help them counter the evolutionary propaganda they face every day.

God is the Master Creator of everything. His handiwork is all around us. Our great Creator put in place all of the laws of physics, biology, and chemistry. These laws were put here for us to see His wisdom and power. In science, we see the hand of God at work more than in any other subject. Romans 1:20 says, "For since the creation of the world His invisible attributes are clearly seen, being understood by the things that are made, even His eternal power and Godhead, so that they [men] are without excuse." We need to help our children see God as Creator of the world around them so they will be able to recognize God and follow Him.

The study of earth science helps us to understand and appreciate this amazing world God gave us. Studying the processes that shape the earth, and exploring the origins of the earth and the universe often brings us into direct conflict with evolutionary theories. This is why it is so critical to teach our children the truth of the Bible, how to evaluate the evidence, how to distinguish fact from theory, and to realize that the evidence, rightly interpreted, supports biblical creation, not evolution.

It's fun to teach earth science! It's interesting too. Rocks, weather, and stars are all around us. Children naturally collect rocks and gaze at the stars. You just need to direct their curiosity.

Finally, teaching earth science is easy. It's where you live. You won't have to try to find strange materials for experiments or do dangerous things to learn about the earth.

How Do I Teach Science?

In order to teach any subject you need to understand how people learn. Most people, and children in particular, have a dominant or preferred learning style in which they absorb and retain information more easily.

If a student's dominant style is:

Auditory
He or she needs not only to hear the information, but to hear him or herself say it. This child needs oral presentation as well as oral drill and repetition.
Visual
The student needs things he or she can see. This child responds well to flashcards, pictures, charts, models, etc.
Kinesthetic
He or she needs active participation. This child remembers best through games, hands-on activities, experiments, and field trips.

Also, some people are more relational while others are more analytical. The relational student needs to know why this subject is important, and how it will affect him or her personally. The analytical student, however, wants just the facts.

If you are trying to teach more than one student, you will probably have to deal with more than one learning style. Therefore, you need to present your lessons in several different ways so that each student can grasp and retain the information.

Grades 3–8

The first part of each lesson should be completed by all upper elementary and junior high students. This is the main part of the lesson containing a reading section, a hands-on activity that reinforces the ideas in the reading section (blue box), and a review section that provides review questions and application questions.

Grades 6–8

In addition, for middle school/junior high age students, we provide a "Challenge" section that contains more challenging material as well as additional activities and projects for older students (green box).

We have included periodic biographies to help your students appreciate the great men and women who have gone before us in the field of science.

We suggest a threefold approach to each lesson:

Introduce the topic

We give a brief description of the facts. Frequently you will want to add more information than the essentials given in this book. In addition to reading this section aloud (or having older children read it on their own), you may wish to do one or more of the following:

- Read a related book with your students.

- Write things down to help your visual learners.

- Give some history of the subject. We provide some historical sketches to help you, but you may want to add more.

- Ask questions to get your students thinking about the subject.

Make observations and do experiments

- Hands-on projects are suggested for each lesson. This part of each lesson may require help from the teacher.

- Have your students perform the activity by themselves whenever possible.

Review

- The "What did we learn?" section has review questions.

- The "Taking it further" section encourages students to:

  - Draw conclusions

  - Make applications of what was learned

  - Add extended information to what was covered in the lesson

- The "FUN FACT" section adds fun or interesting information.

By teaching all three parts of the lesson, you will be presenting the material in a way that children with any learning style can both relate to and remember.

Also, this approach relates directly to the scientific method and will help your students think more scientifically. The *scientific method* is just a way to examine a subject logically and learn from it. Briefly, the steps of the scientific method are:

1. Learn about a topic.

2. Ask a question.

3. Make a hypothesis (a good guess).

4. Design an experiment to test your hypothesis.

5. Observe the experiment and collect data.

6. Draw conclusions. (Does the data support your hypothesis?)

Note: It's okay to have a "wrong hypothesis." That's how we learn. Be sure to help your students understand why they sometimes get a different result than expected.

Our lessons will help your students begin to approach problems in a logical, scientific way.

How Do I Teach Creation vs. Evolution?

We are constantly bombarded by evolutionary ideas about the earth in books, movies, museums, and even commercials. These raise many questions: What is the big bang? How old is the earth? Do fossils show evolution to be true? Was there really a worldwide flood? When did dinosaurs live? Was there an ice age? How can we teach our children the truth about the origins of the earth? The Bible answers these questions and this book accepts the historical accuracy of the Bible as written. We believe this is the only way we can teach our children to trust that everything God says is true.

There are five common views of the origins of life and the age of the earth:

Historical biblical account	Progressive creation	Gap theory	Theistic evolution	Naturalistic evolution
Each day of creation in Genesis is a normal day of about 24 hours in length, in which God created everything that exists. The earth is only thousands of years old, as determined by the genealogies in the Bible.	The idea that God created various creatures to replace other creatures that died out over millions of years. Each of the days in Genesis represents a long period of time (day-age view) and the earth is billions of years old.	The idea that there was a long, long time between what happened in Genesis 1:1 and what happened in Genesis 1:2. During this time, the "fossil record" was supposed to have formed, and millions of years of earth history supposedly passed.	The idea that God used the process of evolution over millions of years (involving struggle and death) to bring about what we see today.	The view that there is no God and evolution of all life forms happened by purely naturalistic processes over billions of years.

Any theory that tries to combine the evolutionary time frame with creation presupposes that death entered the world before Adam sinned, which contradicts what God has said in His Word. The view that the earth (and its "fossil record") is hundreds of millions of years old damages the gospel message. God's completed creation was "very good" at the end of the sixth day (Genesis 1:31). Death entered this perfect paradise *after* Adam disobeyed God's command. It was the punishment for Adam's sin (Genesis 2:16–17, 3:19; Romans 5:12–19). Thorns appeared when God cursed the ground because of Adam's sin (Genesis 3:18).

The first animal death occurred when God killed at least one animal, shedding its blood, to make clothes for Adam and Eve (Genesis 3:21). If the earth's "fossil record" (filled with death, disease, and thorns) formed over millions of years before Adam appeared (and before he sinned), then death no longer would be the penalty for sin. Death, the "last enemy" (1 Corinthians 15:26), diseases (such as cancer), and thorns would instead be part of the original creation that God labeled "very good." No, it is clear that the "fossil record" formed some time *after* Adam sinned — not many millions of years before. Most fossils were formed as a result of the worldwide Genesis Flood.

When viewed from a biblical perspective, the scientific evidence clearly supports a recent creation by God, and not naturalistic evolution and millions of years. The volume of evidence supporting the biblical creation account is substantial and cannot be adequately covered in this book. If you would like more information on this topic, please see the resource guide in Appendix A. To help get you started, just a few examples of evidence supporting biblical creation are given on the following pages.

Evolutionary Myth: The earth is 4.6 billion years old.

The Truth: Many processes observed today point to a young earth of only a few thousand years. The rate at which the earth's magnetic field is decaying suggests the earth must be less than 10,000 years old. The rate of population growth and the recent emergence of civilization suggests only a few thousand years of human population. And, at the current rate of accumulation, the amount of mud on the sea floor should be many kilometers thick if the earth were billions of years old. However, the average depth of all the mud in the whole ocean is less than 400 meters, giving a maximum age for the earth of not more than 12 million years. All this and more indicates an earth much younger than 4.6 billion years.

John D. Morris, *The Young Earth* (Creation Life Publishers, 1994), pp. 70–71, 83–90. See also www.answersingenesis.org/go/young.

Evolutionary Myth: The universe formed from the big bang.

The Truth: There are many problems with this theory. It does not explain where the initial material came from. It cannot explain what caused that material to fly apart in the first place. And nothing in physics indicates what would make the particles begin to stick together instead of flying off into space forever. The big bang theory contradicts many scientific laws. Because of these problems, some scientists have abandoned the big bang and are attempting to develop new theories to explain the origin of the universe.

Jason Lisle, "Does the Big Bang Fit with the Bible?," in *The New Answers Book 2*, Ken Ham, ed. (Master Books, 2008). See also www. answersingenesis.org/go/big-bang.

Evolutionary Myth: Fossils prove evolution.

The Truth: While Darwin predicted that the fossil record would show numerous transitional fossils, even more than 145 years later, all we have are a handful of disputable examples. For example, there are no fossils showing something that is part way between a dinosaur and a bird. Fossils show that a snail has always been a snail; a squid has always been a squid. God created each animal to reproduce after its kind (Genesis 1:20–25).

Evolutionary Myth: There is not enough water for a worldwide flood.

The Truth: Prior to the Flood, just as today, much of the water was stored beneath the surface of the earth. In addition, Genesis 1 states that the water below was separated from the water above, indicating that the atmosphere may have contained a great deal more water than it does today. Also, it is likely that before the Flood the mountains were not as high as they are today, but that the mountains rose and the valleys sank *after* the Flood began, as Psalm 104:6–9 suggests. At the beginning of the Flood, the fountains of the deep burst forth and it rained for 40 days and nights. This could have provided more than enough water to flood the entire earth. Indeed, if the entire earth's surface were leveled by smoothing out the topography of not only the land surface but also the rock surface on the ocean floor, the waters of the present-day oceans would cover the earth's surface to a depth of 1.7 miles (2.7 kilometers). Fossils have been found on the highest mountain peaks around the world showing that the waters of the Flood did indeed cover the entire earth.

Ken Ham & Tim Lovett, "Was There Really a Noah's Ark and Flood?," in *The New Answers Book 1*, Ken Ham, ed. (Master Books, 2006).

The Truth: There is widespread evidence of glaciers in many parts of the world indicating one ice age. Evolutionists find the cause of the Ice Age a mystery. Obviously, the climate would need to be colder. But global cooling by itself is not enough, because then there would be less evaporation, so less snow. How is it possible to have both a cold climate and lots of evaporation? The Ice Age was most likely an aftermath of Noah's Flood. When "all the fountains of the great deep" broke up, much hot water and lava would have poured directly into the oceans. This would have warmed the oceans, increasing evaporation. At the same time, much volcanic ash in the air after the Flood would have blocked out much sunlight, cooling the land. So the Flood would have produced the necessary combination of increased evaporation from the warmed oceans and cool continental climate from the volcanic ash in the air. This would have resulted in increased snowfall over the continents. With the snow falling faster than it melted, ice sheets would have built up. The Ice Age probably lasted less than 700 years.

Michael Oard, *Frozen in Time* (Master Books, 2004). See also www.answersingenesis.org/go/ice-age.

Evolutionary Myth: Thousands of random changes over millions of years resulted in the earth we see today.

The Truth: The second law of thermodynamics describes how any system tends toward a state of zero entropy or disorder. We observe how everything around us becomes less organized and loses energy. The changes required for the formation of the universe, the planet earth and life, all from disorder, run counter to the physical laws we see at work today. There is no known mechanism to harness the raw energy of the universe and generate the specified complexity we see all around us.

John D. Morris, *The Young Earth* (Creation Life Publishers, 1994), p. 43. See also www.answersingenesis.org/go/thermodynamics.

Despite the claims of many scientists, if you examine the evidence objectively, it is obvious that evolution and millions of years have not been proven. You can be confident that if you teach that what the Bible says is true, you won't go wrong. Instill in your student a confidence in the truth of the Bible in all areas. If scientific thought seems to contradict the Bible, realize that scientists often make mistakes, but God does not lie. At one time scientists believed that the earth was the center of the universe, that living things could spring from non-living things, and that blood-letting was good for the body. All of these were believed to be scientific facts but have since been disproved. The Word of God remains true. If we use modern "science" to interpret the Bible, what will happen to our faith in God's Word when scientists change their theories yet again?

Integrating the Seven C's

The Seven C's is a framework in which all of history, and the future to come, can be placed. As we go through our daily routines we may not understand how the details of life connect with the truth that we find in the Bible. This is also the case for students. When discussing the importance of the Bible you may find yourself telling students that the Bible is relevant in everyday activities. But how do we help the younger generation see that? The Seven C's are intended to help.

The Seven C's can be used to develop a biblical worldview in students, young or old. Much more than entertaining stories and religious teachings, the Bible has real connections to our everyday life. It may be hard, at first, to see how many connections there are, but with practice, the daily relevance of God's Word will come alive. Let's look at the Seven C's of History and how each can be connected to what the students are learning.

Creation

God perfectly created the heavens, the earth, and all that is in them in six normal-length days around 6,000 years ago.

This teaching is foundational to a biblical world-view and can be put into the context of any subject. In science, the amazing design that we see in nature — whether in the veins of a leaf or the complexity of your hand — is all the handiwork of God. Virtually all of the lessons in *God's Design for Science* can be related to God's creation of the heavens and earth.

Other contexts include:

Natural laws—any discussion of a law of nature naturally leads to God's creative power.

DNA and information—the information in every living thing was created by God's supreme intelligence.

Mathematics—the laws of mathematics reflect the order of the Creator.

Biological diversity—the distinct kinds of animals that we see were created during the Creation Week, not as products of evolution.

Art—the creativity of man is demonstrated through various art forms.

History—all time scales can be compared to the biblical time scale extending back about 6,000 years.

Ecology—God has called mankind to act as stewards over His creation.

Corruption

After God completed His perfect creation, Adam disobeyed God by eating the forbidden fruit. As a result, sin and death entered the world, and the world has been in decay since that time. This point is evident throughout the world that we live in. The struggle for survival in animals, the death of loved ones, and the violence all around us are all examples of the corrupting influence of sin.

Other contexts include:

Genetics—the mutations that lead to diseases, cancer, and variation within populations are the result of corruption.

Biological relationships—predators and parasites result from corruption.

History—wars and struggles between mankind, exemplified in the account of Cain and Abel, are a result of sin.

Catastrophe

God was grieved by the wickedness of mankind and judged this wickedness with a global flood. The Flood covered the entire surface of the earth and killed all air-breathing creatures that were not aboard the Ark. The eight people and the animals aboard the Ark replenished the earth after God delivered them from the catastrophe.

The catastrophe described in the Bible would naturally leave behind much evidence. The studies of geology and of the biological diversity of animals on the planet are two of the most obvious applications of this event. Much of scientific understanding is based on how a scientist views the events of the Genesis Flood.

Other contexts include:

Biological diversity—all of the birds, mammals, and other air-breathing animals have populated the earth from the original kinds which left the Ark.

Geology—the layers of sedimentary rock seen in roadcuts, canyons, and other geologic features are testaments to the global Flood.

Geography—features like mountains, valleys, and plains were formed as the floodwaters receded.

Physics—rainbows are a perennial sign of God's faithfulness and His pledge to never flood the entire earth again.

Fossils—most fossils are a result of the Flood rapidly burying plants and animals.

Plate tectonics—the rapid movement of the earth's plates likely accompanied the Flood.

Global warming/Ice Age—both of these items are likely a result of the activity of the Flood. The warming we are experiencing today has been present since the peak of the Ice Age (with variations over time).

Confusion

God commanded Noah and his descendants to spread across the earth. The refusal to obey this command and the building of the tower at Babel caused God to judge this sin. The common language of the people was confused and they spread across the globe as groups with a common language. All people are truly of "one blood" as descendants of Noah and, originally, Adam.

The confusion of the languages led people to scatter across the globe. As people settled in new areas, the traits they carried with them became concentrated in those populations. Traits like dark skin were beneficial in the tropics while other traits benefited populations in northern climates, and distinct people groups, not races, developed.

Other contexts include:

Genetics—the study of human DNA has shown that there is little difference in the genetic makeup of the so-called "races."

Languages—there are about seventy language groups from which all modern languages have developed.

Archaeology—the presence of common building structures, like pyramids, around the world confirms the biblical account.

Literature—recorded and oral records tell of similar events relating to the Flood and the dispersion at Babel.

Christ

God did not leave mankind without a way to be redeemed from its sinful state. The Law was given to Moses to show how far away man is from God's standard of perfection. Rather than the sacrifices, which only covered sins, people needed a Savior to take away their sin. This was accomplished when Jesus Christ came to earth to live a perfect life and, by that obedience, was able to be the sacrifice to satisfy God's wrath for all who believe.

The deity of Christ and the amazing plan that was set forth before the foundation of the earth is the core of Christian doctrine. The earthly life of Jesus was the fulfillment of many prophecies and confirms the truthfulness of the Bible. His miracles and presence in human form demonstrate that God is both intimately concerned with His creation and able to control it in an absolute way.

Other contexts include:

Psychology—popular secular psychology teaches of the inherent goodness of man, but Christ has lived the only perfect life. Mankind needs a Savior to redeem it from its unrighteousness.

Biology—Christ's virgin birth demonstrates God's sovereignty over nature.

Physics—turning the water into wine and the feeding of the five thousand demonstrate Christ's deity and His sovereignty over nature.

History—time is marked (in the western world) based on the birth of Christ despite current efforts to change the meaning.

Art—much art is based on the life of Christ and many of the masters are known for these depictions, whether on canvas or in music.

Cross

Because God is perfectly just and holy, He must punish sin. The sinless life of Jesus Christ was offered as a substitutionary sacrifice for all of those who will repent and put their faith in the Savior. After His death on the Cross, He defeated death by rising on the third day and is now seated at the right hand of God.

The events surrounding the crucifixion and resurrection have a most significant place in the life of Christians. Though there is no way to scientifically prove the resurrection, there is likewise no way to prove the stories of evolutionary history. These are matters of faith founded in the truth of God's Word and His character. The eyewitness testimony of over 500 people and the written Word of God provide the basis for our belief.

Other contexts include:

Biology—the biological details of the crucifixion can be studied alongside the anatomy of the human body.

History—the use of crucifixion as a method of punishment was short-lived in historical terms and not known at the time it was prophesied.

Art—the crucifixion and resurrection have inspired many wonderful works of art.

Consummation

God, in His great mercy, has promised that He will restore the earth to its original state — a world without death, suffering, war, and disease. The corruption introduced by Adam's sin will be removed. Those who have repented and put their trust in the completed work of Christ on the Cross will experience life in this new heaven and earth. We will be able to enjoy and worship God forever in a perfect place.

This future event is a little more difficult to connect with academic subjects. However, the hope of a life in God's presence and in the absence of sin can be inserted in discussions of human conflict, disease, suffering, and sin in general.

Other contexts include:

History—in discussions of war or human conflict the coming age offers hope.

Biology—the violent struggle for life seen in the predator-prey relationships will no longer taint the earth.

Medicine—while we struggle to find cures for diseases and alleviate the suffering of those enduring the effects of the Curse, we ultimately place our hope in the healing that will come in the eternal state.

The preceding examples are given to provide ideas for integrating the Seven C's of History into a broad range of curriculum activities. The first seven lessons of this curriculum cover the Seven C's and will establish a solid understanding of the true history, and future, of the universe.

Even if you use other curricula, you can still incorporate the Seven C's teaching into those. Using this approach will help students make firm connections between biblical events and every aspect of the world around them, and they will begin to develop a truly biblical worldview and not just add pieces of the Bible to what they learn in "the real world."

First Semester Suggested Daily Schedule

Date	Day	Assignment	Due Date	✓	Grade
		First Semester-First Quarter			
Week 1	Day 1	Our Weather & Water Unit 1: Atmosphere & Meteorology Read Lesson 1: A Christian View of Weather Pages 14–15 • *God's Design: Heaven & Earth* • (GDHE) Complete Worksheet • Pages 25–26 • *Teacher Guide* • (TG)			
	Day 2	Read Lesson 2: Structure of the Atmosphere • Pages 16–18 • (GDHE) Complete Worksheet • Pages 27–28 • (TG)			
	Day 3	Read Lesson 3: The Weight of Air • Pages 19–21• (GDHE) Complete Worksheet • Pages 29–30 • (TG)			
	Day 4	Read Special Feature: Discovery of Air • Page 22 • (GDHE)			
	Day 5				
Week 2	Day 6	Read Lesson 4: The Study of Weather • Pages 23–25 • (GDHE) Complete Worksheet • Pages 31–32 • (TG)			
	Day 7	Complete **Our Weather & Water Quiz 1** (Lessons 1–4) Pages 267–268 • (TG)			
	Day 8	Our Weather & Water Unit 2: Ancient Weather & Climate Read Lesson 5: Weather vs. Climate • Pages 27–30 • (GDHE) Complete Worksheets • Pages 33–36 • (TG)			
	Day 9	Read Lesson 6: Pre-Flood Climate • Pages 31–33 • (GDHE) Complete Worksheet • Pages 37–38 • (TG)			
	Day 10				
Week 3	Day 11	Read Lesson 7: Climate Changes Due to the Genesis Flood Pages 34–37 • (GDHE) Complete Worksheet • Pages 39–40 • (TG)			
	Day 12	Read Special Feature: Weather and the Bible • Pages 38–39 • (GDHE)			
	Day 13	Read Lesson 8: Global Warming • Pages 40–42 • (GDHE) Complete Worksheet • Pages 41–42 • (TG)			
	Day 14	Complete **Our Weather & Water Quiz 2** (Lessons 5–8) Pages 269–270 • (TG)			
	Day 15				
Week 4	Day 16	Our Weather & Water Unit 3: Clouds Read Lesson 9: Water Cycle • Pages 44–46 • (GDHE) Complete Worksheet • Pages 43–44 • (TG)			
	Day 17	Read Lesson 10: Cloud Formation • Pages 47–49 • (GDHE) Complete Worksheet • Pages 45–46 • (TG)			
	Day 18	Read Lesson 11: Cloud Types • Pages 50–52 • (GDHE) Complete Worksheet • Pages 47–48 • (TG)			
	Day 19	Read Lesson 12: Precipitation • Pages 53–56 • (GDHE) Complete Worksheet • Pages 49–50 • (TG)			
	Day 20				

Date	Day	Assignment	Due Date	✓	Grade
Week 5	Day 21	Read Special Feature: The Dust Bowl • Pages 57–58 • (GDHE)			
	Day 22	Complete **Our Weather & Water Quiz 3** (Lessons 9–12) Pages 271–272 • (TG)			
	Day 23	Our Weather & Water Unit 4: Storms Read Lesson 13: Air Masses & Weather Fronts Pages 60–62 • (GDHE) Complete Worksheet • Pages 51–52 • (TG)			
	Day 24	Read Lesson 14: Wind • Pages 63–66 • (GDHE) Complete Worksheet • Pages 53–54 • (TG)			
	Day 25				
Week 6	Day 26	Read Lesson 15: Thunderstorms • Pages 67–70 • (GDHE) Complete Worksheet • Pages 55–56 • (TG)			
	Day 27	Read Lesson 16: Tornadoes • Pages 71–74 • (GDHE) Complete Worksheet • Pages 57–58 • (TG)			
	Day 28	Read Lesson 17: Hurricanes • Pages 75–79 • (GDHE) Complete Worksheet • Pages 59–60 • (TG)			
	Day 29	Complete **Our Weather & Water Quiz 4** (Lessons 13–17) Pages 273–274 • (TG)			
	Day 30				
Week 7	Day 31	Our Weather & Water Unit 5: Weather Information Read Lesson 18: Gathering Weather Information Pages 81–85 • (GDHE) Complete Worksheet • Pages 61–62 • (TG)			
	Day 32	Read Special Feature: Weather Myths • Pages 86–87 • (GDHE)			
	Day 33	Read Lesson 19: More Weather Instruments • Pages 88–92 • (GDHE) Complete Worksheet • Pages 63–64 • (TG)			
	Day 34	Read Lesson 20: Reporting & Analyzing Weather Information Pages 93–95 • (GDHE) Complete Worksheet • Pages 65–66 • (TG)			
	Day 35				
Week 8	Day 36	Read Lesson 21: Forecasting the Weather • Pages 96–98 • (GDHE) Complete Worksheet • Pages 67–68 • (TG)			
	Day 37	Read Lesson 22: Weather Station: Final Project Pages 99–100 • (GDHE) Complete Worksheet • Pages 69–71 • (TG)			
	Day 38	Complete **Our Weather & Water Quiz 5** (Lessons 18–22) Pages 275–276 • (TG)			
	Day 39	Our Weather & Water Unit 6: Ocean Movement Read Lesson 23: Overview of the Oceans • Pages 102–104 • (GDHE) Complete Worksheet • Pages 73–74 • (TG)			
	Day 40				
Week 9	Day 41	Read Lesson 24: Composition of Seawater Pages 105–107 • (GDHE) Complete Worksheet • Pages 75–76 • (TG)			
	Day 42	Read Lesson 25: Ocean Currents • Pages 108–111 • (GDHE) Complete Worksheet • Pages 77–78 • (TG)			
	Day 43	Read Special Feature: El Niño • Pages 112–113 • (GDHE)			
	Day 44	Read Lesson 26: Waves • Pages 114–117 • (GDHE) Complete Worksheet • Pages 79–80 • (TG)			
	Day 45				

Date	Day	Assignment	Due Date	✓	Grade
		First Semester-Second Quarter			
Week 1	Day 46	Read Lesson 27: Tides • Pages 118–120 • (GDHE) Complete Worksheet • Pages 81–82 • (TG)			
	Day 47	Read Lesson 28: Wave Erosion • Pages 121–123 • (GDHE) Complete Worksheet • Pages 83–84 • (TG)			
	Day 48	Read Lesson 29: Energy from the Ocean • Pages 124–125 • (GDHE) Complete Worksheet • Pages 85–86 • (TG)			
	Day 49	Complete **Our Weather & Water Quiz 6** (Lessons 23–29) Pages 277–278 • (TG)			
	Day 50				
Week 2	Day 51	Our Weather & Water Unit 7: Sea Floor Read Lesson 30: Sea Exploration • Pages 127–130 • (GDHE) Complete Worksheet • Pages 87–88 • (TG)			
	Day 52	Read Lesson 31: Geography of the Ocean Floor Pages 131–134 • (GDHE) Complete Worksheet • Pages 89–90 • (TG)			
	Day 53	Read Lesson 32: Ocean Zones • Pages 135–137 • (GDHE) Complete Worksheet • Pages 91–92 • (TG)			
	Day 54	Read Special Feature: Intertidal Zones • Page 138 • (GDHE)			
	Day 55				
Week 3	Day 56	Read Lesson 33: Vents & Smokers • Pages 139–141 • (GDHE) Complete Worksheet • Pages 93–94 • (TG)			
	Day 57	Read Lesson 34: Coral Reefs • Pages 142–144 • (GDHE) Complete Worksheet • Pages 95–96 • (TG)			
	Day 58	Read Lesson 35: Conclusion • Page 145 • (GDHE) Complete Worksheet • Page 97 • (TG)			
	Day 59	Complete **Our Weather & Water Quiz 7** (Lessons 30–34) Pages 279–280 • (TG)			
	Day 60				
Week 4	Day 61	Complete **Our Weather & Water Final Exam** (Lessons 1–34) Pages 281–284 • (TG)			
	Day 62	Our Universe Unit 1: Space Models Read Lesson 1: Introduction to Astronomy Pages 154–155 • (GDHE) Complete Worksheet • Pages 101–103 • (TG)			
	Day 63	Read Lesson 2: Space Models • Pages 156–160 • (GDHE) Complete Worksheet • Pages 105–106 • (TG)			
	Day 64	Read Special Feature: Nicolaus Copernicus • Pages 161–162 • (GDHE)			
	Day 65				
Week 5	Day 66	Read Lesson 3: The Earth's Movement • Pages 163–166 • (GDHE) Complete Worksheet • Pages 107–109 • (TG)			
	Day 67	Read Lesson 4: Tools for Studying Space • Pages 167–172 • (GDHE) Complete Worksheet • Pages 111–112 • (TG)			
	Day 68	Read Special Feature: Galileo Galilei • Pages 173–174 • (GDHE)			
	Day 69	Complete **Our Universe Quiz 1** (Lessons 1–4) Pages 287–288 • (TG)			
	Day 70				

Date	Day	Assignment	Due Date	✓	Grade
Week 6	Day 71	Our Universe Unit 2: Outer Space Read Lesson 5: Overview of the Universe • Pages 176–178 • (GDHE) Complete Worksheet • Pages 113–114 • (TG)			
	Day 72	Read Lesson 6: Stars • Pages 179–181 • (GDHE) Complete Worksheet • Pages 115–116 • (TG)			
	Day 73	Read Lesson 7: Heavenly Bodies • Pages 182–185 • (GDHE) Complete Worksheet • Pages 117–118 • (TG)			
	Day 74	Read Special Feature: Astronomy vs. Astrology • Page 186 • (GDHE)			
	Day 75				
Week 7	Day 76	Read Lesson 8: Asteroids • Pages 187–189 • (GDHE) Complete Worksheet • Pages 119–120 • (TG)			
	Day 77	Read Lesson 9: Comets • Pages 190–192 • (GDHE) Complete Worksheet • Pages 121–122 • (TG)			
	Day 78	Read Lesson 10: Meteors • Pages 193–196 • (GDHE) Complete Worksheet • Pages 123–124 • (TG)			
	Day 79	Complete **Our Universe Quiz 2** (Lessons 5–10) Pages 289–290 • (TG)			
	Day 80				
Week 8	Day 81	Our Universe Unit 3: Sun & Moon Read Lesson 11: Overview of Our Solar System Pages 198–201 • (GDHE) Complete Worksheet • Pages 125–126 • (TG)			
	Day 82	Read Lesson 12: Our Sun • Pages 202–204 • (GDHE) Complete Worksheet • Pages 127–128 • (TG)			
	Day 83	Read Lesson 13: Structure of the Sun • Pages 205–208 • (GDHE) Complete Worksheet • Pages 129–130 • (TG)			
	Day 84	Read Lesson 14: Solar Eclipse • Pages 209–211 • (GDHE) Complete Worksheet • Pages 131–132 • (TG)			
	Day 85				
Week 9	Day 86	Read Lesson 15: Solar Energy • Pages 212–214 • (GDHE) Complete Worksheet • Pages 133–135 • (TG)			
	Day 87	Read Lesson 16: Our Moon • Pages 215–217 • (GDHE) Complete Worksheet • Pages 137–138 • (TG)			
	Day 88	Read Special Feature: Newton & the Apple Pages 218–219 • (GDHE)			
	Day 89	Read Lesson 17: Motion & Phases of the Moon Pages 220–223 • (GDHE) Complete Worksheets • Pages 139–142 • (TG)			
	Day 90				
		Mid-Term Grade			

Second Semester Suggested Daily Schedule

Date	Day	Assignment	Due Date	✓	Grade
		Second Semester–Third Quarter			
Week 1	Day 91	Read Lesson 18: Origin of the Moon • Pages 224–226 • (GDHE) Complete Worksheet • Pages 143–144 • (TG)			
	Day 92	Complete **Our Universe Quiz 3** (Lessons 11–18) Pages 291–292 • (TG)			
	Day 93	Our Universe Unit 4: Planets Read Lesson 19: Mercury • Pages 228–230 • (GDHE) Complete Worksheet • Pages 145–146 • (TG)			
	Day 94	Read Lesson 20: Venus • Pages 231–233 • (GDHE) Complete Worksheets • Pages 147–149 • (TG)			
	Day 95				
Week 2	Day 96	Read Lesson 21: Earth • Pages 234–236 • (GDHE) Complete Worksheets • Pages 151–152 • (TG)			
	Day 97	Read Lesson 22: Mars • Pages 237–239 • (GDHE) Complete Worksheets • Pages 153–154 • (TG)			
	Day 98	Read Lesson 23: Jupiter • Pages 240–242 • (GDHE) Complete Worksheets • Pages 155–156 • (TG)			
	Day 99	Read Lesson 24: Saturn • Pages 243–245 • (GDHE) Complete Worksheets • Pages 157–158 • (TG)			
	Day 100				
Week 3	Day 101	Read Lesson 25: Uranus • Pages 246–248 • (GDHE) Complete Worksheets • Pages 159–160 • (TG)			
	Day 102	Read Lesson 26: Neptune • Pages 249–251 • (GDHE) Complete Worksheets • Pages 161–162 • (TG)			
	Day 103	Read Lesson 27: Pluto & Eris • Pages 252–254 • (GDHE) Complete Worksheets • Pages 163–164 • (TG)			
	Day 104	Read Special Feature: Planet Statistics • Page 255 • (GDHE)			
	Day 105				
Week 4	Day 106	Complete **Our Universe Quiz 4** (Lessons 19–27) Pages 293–294 • (TG)			
	Day 107	Our Universe Unit 5: Space Program Read Lesson 28: NASA • Pages 257–260 • (GDHE) Complete Worksheet • Pages 165–166 • (TG)			
	Day 108	Read Lesson 29: Space Exploration • Pages 261–265 • (GDHE) Complete Worksheet • Pages 167–168 • (TG)			
	Day 109	Read Lesson 30: Apollo Program • Pages 266–270 • (GDHE) Complete Worksheet • Pages 169–170 • (TG)			
	Day 110				

Date	Day	Assignment	Due Date	✓	Grade
Week 5	Day 111	Read Lesson 31: The Space Shuttle • Pages 271–274 • (GDHE) Complete Worksheet • Pages 171–172 • (TG)			
	Day 112	Read Special Feature: Rick D. Husband • Page 275 • (GDHE)			
	Day 113	Read Lesson 32: International Space Station Pages 276–279 • (GDHE) Complete Worksheet • Pages 173–174 • (TG)			
	Day 114	Read Lesson 33: Astronauts • Pages 280–282 • (GDHE) Complete Worksheet • Pages 175–176 • (TG)			
	Day 115				
Week 6	Day 116	Read Special Feature: Jeffery Nels Williams Pages 283–284 • (GDHE)			
	Day 117	Read Lesson 34: Solar System Model: Final Project Pages 285–286 • (GDHE) Complete Worksheet • Pages 177–178 • (TG)			
	Day 118	Read Lesson 35: Conclusion • Pages 287–288 • (GDHE) Complete Worksheet • Page 179 • (TG)			
	Day 119	Complete **Our Universe Quiz 5** (Lessons 28–33) Pages 295–296 • (TG)			
	Day 120				
Week 7	Day 121	Complete **Our Universe Final Exam** (Lessons 1–34) Pages 297–299 • (TG)			
	Day 122	Our Planet Earth Unit 1: Origins & Glaciers • Read Lesson 1: Introduction to Earth Science • Pages 294–297 • (GDHE) Complete Worksheet • Pages 183–184 • (TG)			
	Day 123	Read Lesson 2: Introduction to Geology Pages 298–300 • (GDHE) Complete Worksheet • Pages 185–186 • (TG)			
	Day 124	Read Lesson 3: The Earth's History • Pages 301–304 • (GDHE) Complete Worksheet • Pages 187–188 • (TG)			
	Day 125				
Week 8	Day 126	Read Special Feature: Dating Methods Pages 305–306 • (GDHE)			
	Day 127	Read Lesson 4: The Genesis Flood • Pages 307–308 • (GDHE) Complete Worksheet • Pages 189–190 • (TG)			
	Day 128	Read Special Feature: The Search for Noah's Ark Pages 309–310 • (GDHE)			
	Day 129	Read Lesson 5: The Great Ice Age • Pages 311–313 • (GDHE) Complete Worksheets • Pages 191–194 • (TG)			
	Day 130				
Week 9	Day 131	Read Lesson 6: Glaciers • Pages 314–317 • (GDHE) Complete Worksheet • Pages 195–196 • (TG)			
	Day 132	Read Special Feature: Sir Ernest Shackleton & the *Endurance* Pages 318–319 • (GDHE)			
	Day 133	Read Lesson 7: Movement of Glaciers • Pages 320–322 • (GDHE) Complete Worksheet • Pages 197–198 • (TG)			
	Day 134	Complete **Our Planet Earth Quiz 1** (Lessons 1–7) Pages 303–304 • (TG)			
	Day 135				

Date	Day	Assignment	Due Date	✓	Grade
Week 1	Day 136	Our Planet Earth Unit 2: Rocks & Minerals Read Lesson 8: Design of the Earth • Pages 324–327 • (GDHE) Complete Worksheet • Pages 199–200 • (TG)			
	Day 137	Read Lesson 9: Rocks • Pages 328–330 • (GDHE) Complete Worksheet • Pages 201–202 • (TG)			
	Day 138	Read Lesson 10: Igneous Rocks • Pages 331–334 • (GDHE) Complete Worksheet • Pages 203–204 • (TG)			
	Day 139	Read Lesson 11: Sedimentary Rocks • Pages 335–338 • (GDHE) Complete Worksheet • Pages 205–206 • (TG)			
	Day 140				
Week 2	Day 141	Read Lesson 12: Fossils • Pages 339–341 • (GDHE) Complete Worksheet • Pages 207–208 • (TG)			
	Day 142	Read Lesson 13: Fossil Fuels • Pages 342–345 • (GDHE) Complete Worksheet • Pages 209–210 • (TG)			
	Day 143	Read Lesson 14: Metamorphic Rocks • Pages 346–347 • (GDHE) Complete Worksheets • Pages 211–214 • (TG)			
	Day 144	Read Special Feature: Artificial Islands Pages 348–349 • (GDHE)			
	Day 145				
Week 3	Day 146	Read Lesson 15: Minerals • Pages 350–352 • (GDHE) Complete Worksheet • Pages 215–216 • (TG)			
	Day 147	Read Lesson 16: Identifying Minerals • Pages 353–355 • (GDHE) Complete Worksheets • Pages 217–220 • (TG)			
	Day 148	Read Lesson 17: Valuable Minerals • Pages 356–358 • (GDHE) Complete Worksheet • Pages 221–222 • (TG)			
	Day 149	Read Lesson 18: Natural & Artificial Gems Pages 359–360 • (GDHE) Complete Worksheets • Pages 223–224 • (TG)			
	Day 150				
Week 4	Day 151	Complete **Our Planet Earth Quiz 2** (Lessons 8–18) Pages 305–306 • (TG)			
	Day 152	Our Planet Earth Unit 3: Mountains & Movement Read Lesson 19: Plate Tectonics • Pages 362–365 • (GDHE) Complete Worksheet • Pages 225–226 • (TG)			
	Day 153	Read Lesson 20: Mountains • Pages 366–367 • (GDHE) Complete Worksheets • Pages 227–230 • (TG)			
	Day 154	Read Lesson 21: Types of Mountains • Pages 368–371 • (GDHE) Complete Worksheet • Pages 231–232 • (TG)			
	Day 155				

Date	Day	Assignment	Due Date	✓	Grade
Week 5	Day 156	Read Lesson 22: Earthquakes • Pages 372–376 • (GDHE) Complete Worksheets • Pages 233–234 • (TG)			
	Day 157	Read Lesson 23: Detecting & Predicting Earthquakes Pages 377–379 • (GDHE) Complete Worksheet • Pages 235–236 • (TG)			
	Day 158	Read Lesson 24: Volcanoes • Pages 380–382 • (GDHE) Complete Worksheet • Pages 237–238 • (TG)			
	Day 159	Read Special Feature: Mt. Vesuvius • Pages 383–384 • (GDHE)			
	Day 160				
Week 6	Day 161	Read Lesson 25: Volcano Types • Pages 385–388 • (GDHE) Complete Worksheet • Pages 239–240 • (TG)			
	Day 162	Read Lesson 26: Mount St. Helens • Pages 389–391 • (GDHE) Complete Worksheets • Pages 241–242 • (TG)			
	Day 163	Complete **Our Planet Earth Quiz 3** (Lessons 19–26) Pages 307–308 • (TG)			
	Day 164	Our Planet Earth Unit 4: Water & Erosion Read Lesson 27: Geysers • Pages 393–396 • (GDHE) Complete Worksheet • Pages 243–244 • (TG)			
	Day 165				
Week 7	Day 166	Read Lesson 28: Weathering & Erosion Pages 397–398 • (GDHE) Complete Worksheets • Pages 245–248 • (TG)			
	Day 167	Read Lesson 29: Mass Wasting • Pages 399–401 • (GDHE) Complete Worksheet • Pages 249–250 • (TG)			
	Day 168	Read Lesson 30: Stream Erosion • Pages 402–405 • (GDHE) Complete Worksheet • Pages 251–252 • (TG)			
	Day 169	Read Lesson 31: Soil • Pages 406–408 • (GDHE) Complete Worksheets • Pages 253–255 • (TG)			
	Day 170				
Week 8	Day 171	Read Lesson 32: Grand Canyon • Pages 409–411 • (GDHE) Complete Worksheet • Pages 257–258 • (TG)			
	Day 172	Read Lesson 33: Caves • Pages 412–414 • (GDHE) Complete Worksheet • Pages 259–260 • (TG)			
	Day 173	Read Lesson 34: Rocks & Minerals Collection: Final Project Pages 415–416 • (GDHE) Complete Worksheet • Pages 261–262 • (TG)			
	Day 174	Read Lesson 35: Conclusion • Page 417 • (GDHE) Complete Worksheet • Page 263 • (TG)			
	Day 175				
Week 9	Day 176	Review Day for Quiz 4			
	Day 177	Complete **Our Planet Earth Quiz 4** (Lessons 27–34) Pages 309–310 • (TG)			
	Day 178	Review Day for Final Exam			
	Day 179	Complete **Our Planet Earth Final Exam** (Lessons 1–34) Pages 311–314 • (TG)			
	Day 180				
		Final Grade			

Weather & Water Worksheets

for Use with

Our Weather & Water

(*God's Design: Heaven & Earth*)

1   A Christian View of Weather

What does the Bible say?

 Supply list – Weather reports

☐ Copy of "Weather Across the Country" worksheet

☐ Newspaper or Internet weather report

Supplies for Challenge – Bible-believing scientists

☐ Research materials on various Christian scientists

What did we learn?

1. Is there a Christian view of weather?

2. What three events described in the Bible have greatly affected the weather on earth?

3. List three things you can learn about the weather from a newspaper weather report.

Taking it further

1. Why is it important to have a Christian view of weather?

2. What are some geographical or physical characteristics that affect the weather in a particular area?

🔬 Weather Across the Country Worksheet

City	High temperature	Low temperature	Weather conditions
San Francisco, CA			
Las Vegas, NV			
Phoenix, AZ			
Denver, CO			
Houston, TX			
St. Louis, MO			
Chicago, IL			
Miami, FL			
Atlanta, GA			
Philadelphia, PA			
Washington, D.C.			

1. How does the weather in your town compare to the weather in other cities across the country?

2. Why do you think the weather is so different from one city to another?

2 Structure of the Atmosphere

Layers above the earth

🧪 Supply list – Properties of air

☐ Candle

☐ Glass jar

☐ Modeling clay

☐ Matches or lighter

☐ Dish

🎖 Supplies for Challenge – Atmospheric temperature

☐ Graph paper

☐ Pencil or pen

☐ Atmosphere temperature chart

🧠 What did we learn?

1. What are the two main components of air?

2. What are the five levels of the atmosphere?

3. What are some ways that the atmosphere protects us?

🚀 Taking it further

1. How would the earth be different if there were a higher concentration of oxygen?

2. What would happen if the nitrogen in the atmosphere was replaced with a more reactive element, such as carbon?

3   The Weight of Air

It has weight?

🧪 Supply list – Demonstrating the weight of air

☐ Yard or meter stick

☐ 2 identical balloons

☐ Tape

☐ String

🏅 Supplies for Challenge – Air pressure

☐ Wide mouth jar

☐ Plastic grocery bag

☐ String or rubberband

🧠 What did we learn?

1. What causes air to have weight?

2. How much air pressure do we experience at sea level?

3. Why don't we feel the weight of the air molecules?

4. Do you expect air pressure to be the same at all locations in the world?

🚀 Taking it further

1. Why is it important that air has weight?

2. Why must aircraft be pressurized when flying at high altitudes?

 # The Study of Weather

An introduction to meteorology

🧪 Supply list – Making air currents

☐ Baking dish (white or light color works best)

☐ Styrofoam™ cups

☐ Food coloring

☐ Ice

☐ Boiling water

🏅 Supplies for Challenge – Weather ingredients

☐ Copy of "Weather Ingredients" worksheet

🧠 What did we learn?

1. What is meteorology?

2. What are the five important conditions in the troposphere that meteorologists study?

🚀 Taking it further

1. Why are meteorologists interested in studying the conditions of the troposphere?

2. How does the sun heat areas of the earth that do not receive much direct sunlight?

Name _____   Date_____

🏅 Weather Ingredients Worksheet

See if you can fill in each space in the chart below with a word that starts with each letter of the word "WEATHER." Each word should somehow demonstrate how that weather ingredient contributes to the weather that we experience. There is more than one possible answer for each square. You probably can't fill in every space, but do your best.

Here is one word to help get you started. Under *Earth* for *W* you could put "winter" because the tilt of the earth contributes to the seasons we experience.

	Earth	Sun	Air	Water
W	Winter			
E				
A				
T				
H				
E				
R				

5 Weather vs. Climate

What's the difference?

🧪 Supply list – Weather vs. climate

☐ Copy of "Weather vs. Climate" worksheet

☐ Newspaper or Internet weather report

☐ World atlas

🎖 Supplies for Challenge – Factors affecting climate

☐ Copy of "World Map"

☐ Colored pencils

☐ World atlas

🧠 What did we learn?

1. What is weather?

2. What is climate?

3. What are the five major climates found on earth?

🚀 Taking it further

1. How does the Gobi Desert help create the monsoon?

2. Which of the following phrases describe weather (w) and which describe climate (c)?

   Cloudy with a chance of rain: _____

   Average of 20 inches of rain per year: _____

   Average summer temperature of 70°F: _____

   3 inches of snow in the past 24 hours: _____

Name _____   Date_____

⚗️ Weather vs. Climate Worksheet

One place that you can find climate information is in a world atlas. Most atlases show maps with climate information, such as average temperatures and average rainfall at various seasons. Use a world atlas to help you locate a country whose primary climate is shown on the chart below.

Country	Climate
	Polar
	Desert
	Tropical
	Subtropical
	Temperate

One place that you can find weather information is in your local newspaper. Check for each of the following items of information in the weather section of your newspaper (or online).

Weather item	Yes/No	If yes, record information
Today's expected high and low temperatures		
Yesterday's actual high and low temperatures		
Record high and low temperatures for yesterday's date		
Precipitation amounts		
Location of high and low pressure systems (designated with an H or an L on map)		
Location of warm and cold fronts (shown as lines with half circles or triangles on them)		
High/low temperatures for cities across the country (give one example)		
Local forecast for the next several days		

Name _____

Date _____

World Map

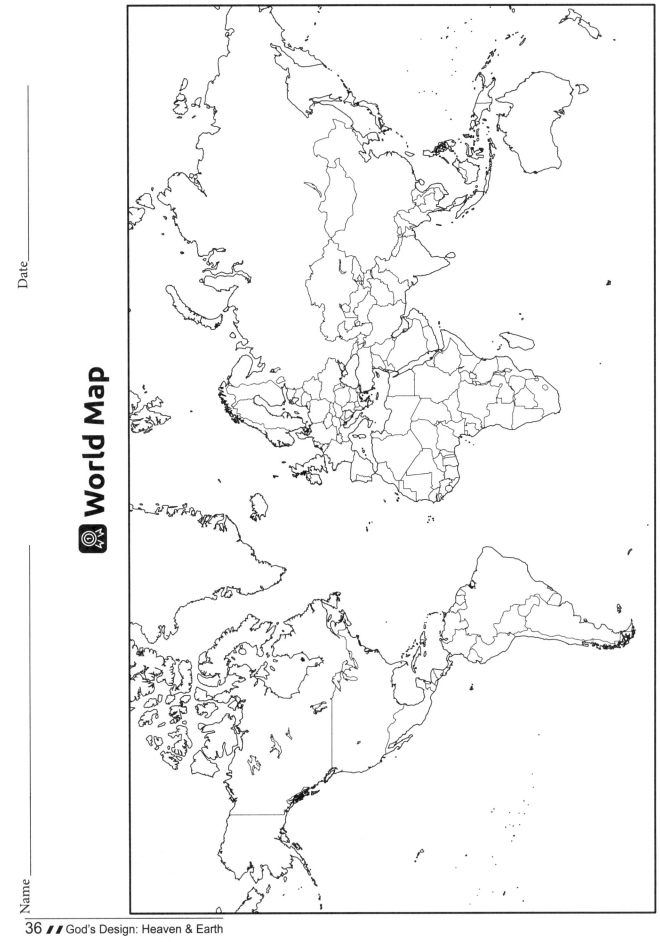

6 Pre-Flood Climate

Was it different?

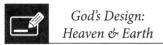 Supply list – Watering without rain

☐ Glass of ice water

☐ Dish of hot water

☐ Mirror

☐ House plant

☐ Plate or shallow dish

Supplies for Challenge – Climate clues

☐ Copy of "Climate Clues" worksheet

What did we learn?

1. Using clues from the Bible and science, what was the climate most likely like on earth before the Flood?

Taking it further

1. How does the Bible say that plants were watered in the beginning?

2. How might the breaking of the earth's crust have contributed to the Flood?

⬛ Climate Clues Worksheet

When geologists and paleontologists dig up rocks and fossils, they get clues to the past. Below are some of the clues that have been found around the world. Answer the questions about each clue then draw some conclusions about the climate before the Flood. You may have to search online or in an atlas or other book to find the answers to some of the questions.

Clue #1

Fossils of swamp cypress trees were found in the Arctic Islands about 600 miles from the North Pole.

1. Where do swamp cypress trees grow today? _____

2. What is the climate like in the Arctic Islands today? _____

3. What possible explanation could there be for how the cypress tree fossils were formed in the Arctic Islands?

   _____

Clue #2

Hippopotamus fossils have been found in the Sahara Desert. Elephant and crocodile fossils have also been found in the Sahara. Cave paintings have been found in the Sahara Desert that show people and villages in the area.

1. Where do hippopotami live today? _____

2. What kind of plant life is required to support elephants? _____

3. Do many people live in villages in the Sahara Desert today? _____

4. What can you conclude about the climate in the Sahara area before the Flood? _____

   _____

Clue #3

Fossils of dinosaurs have been found in Antarctica.

1. What is the climate like in Antarctica today? _____

2. What kind of plant life is required to support dinosaurs? _____

3. What kind of plant life exists in Antarctica today? _____

4. What can you conclude about the climate in Antarctica before the Flood? _____

   _____

7 Climate Changes Due to the Genesis Flood

God's punishment for sin

 **Supply list – Picture of the changing climate**

☐ Paper

☐ Drawing materials (colored pencils, markers, etc.)

What did we learn?

1. What was the earth's climate like before the Flood?

2. What was the climate like after the Flood?

3. Approximately how much of the world was covered with ice during the Ice Age?

4. What two weather conditions are necessary for an ice age to form?

🚀 Taking it further

1. Why did God send a huge flood?

2. What evidence points to a warmer pre-Flood climate?

3. What evidence points to an ice age?

4. Do we see new glaciers forming today?

8 Global Warming

Fact or fiction?

 **Supply list – Global warming in the news**

☐ Articles about global warming or climate change

What did we learn?

1. What is global warming?

2. What is the greenhouse effect?

3. What is the main cause of the greenhouse effect?

4. What amount of greenhouse effect is due to carbon dioxide in the atmosphere?

5. How much has the temperature increased over the past 130 years?

6. Name at least two possible natural causes for increased temperatures.

🚀 Taking it further

1. Why is it important to know what assumptions are made when looking at computer models?

2. Ice core samples from Greenland indicate that rapid climate shifts have occurred in the past. How can your worldview affect the interpretation of this data?

Water Cycle

The ultimate in recycling

Supply list – Drawing the water cycle

☐ Paper

☐ Colored pencils

What did we learn?

1. How does water vapor enter the atmosphere?

2. Which of these processes account for most of the water in the air?

3. How does water get from the atmosphere back to the earth?

 Taking it further

1. What are some factors that affect how fast the water evaporates from the surface of the ocean or lake?

2. Why is it better to water your grass early in the morning rather than later in the day during the summer?

10 Cloud Formation

Pretty white shapes in the sky

🧪 Supply list – Cloud in a bottle

☐ Pan of water

☐ Jar with a lid

☐ Plastic zipper bag

☐ Ice

🎖 Supplies for Challenge – Clouds and snow

☐ Black construction paper

☐ Gloves

☐ Newspaper

☐ Hammer

☐ Flashlight

☐ Towel

☐ 2 shoeboxes (one must be at least 2 inches smaller in each direction than the other)

☐ Lid or cardboard for smaller shoebox

☐ Several small pieces of dry ice

🧠 What did we learn?

1. What is a cloud?

2. What is the dew point of air?

3. What is another name for dew point?

4. How do clouds form?

🚀 Taking it further

1. Often, one side of a mountain range receives much more rain than the other side. Why do you think this happens?

2. Why don't clouds always result in rain?

3. What role do pollen and dust play in cloud formation?

11 Cloud Types

A beautiful variety

⚗️ Supply list – Cloud picture

☐ Blue construction paper

☐ Glue

☐ Cotton balls

🎖️ Supplies for Challenge – Fog formation

☐ Clear 2-liter plastic bottle

☐ Match

☐ Warm water

🧠 What did we learn?

1. What are the two ways that clouds are classified?

2. What are the three main shapes of clouds and how does each look?

3. What are rain clouds called?

🚀 Taking it further

1. What would a fluffy cloud at 0.5 miles (0.8 km) above the earth be called?

2. What would a wispy cloud at 5 miles (8 km) above the earth be called?

🏅 Challenge questions – Fog formation

3. Why does fog form inside the bottle?

4. Why do you think we have you put a match inside the bottle?

12 Precipitation

Rain, rain go away

Supply list – Measuring raindrops

☐ Flour

☐ Pie pan/baking dish

☐ Rain/water

☐ Access to oven

Supplies for Challenge – Acid rain

☐ pH testing paper (optional)

☐ Samples of water from various locations near your home

What did we learn?

1. What are the main types of precipitation?

2. What is the difference between drizzle and rain?

3. What shape do snowflakes have?

4. What is coalescence?

5. What is the difference between sleet and hail?

 **Taking it further**

1. What conditions are necessary for large hailstones to form?

2. How effective is cloud seeding?

13 Air Masses & Weather Fronts

Creating the weather

Supply list – Seeing air pressure

☐ Empty 2-liter plastic bottle

Supplies for Challenge – Movement of weather fronts

☐ Round plate or dish

☐ Syrup

☐ Food coloring

What did we learn?

1. What is an air mass?

2. How do air masses form?

3. How does the air pressure compare between warm and cold air masses?

1.   How would a cold air mass that develops over land be classified?

2.   Why do most weather changes occur along weather fronts?

 # Wind

Hold onto your hat!

🧪 Supply list – Making a wind sock

☐ Metal clothes hanger

☐ Large trash bag

☐ Masking tape

🧠 What did we learn?

1. What is the main cause of wind?

2. What is a jet stream?

3. What are trade winds?

1. Why was it important for sailors of sailing ships to know about trade winds, doldrums, and other prevailing winds?

2. Why does the breeze near the coast blow toward the land in the morning and toward the sea at night?

15 Thunderstorms

Lightning and thunder

 Supply list – Making lightning

☐ Furry stuffed animal

☐ Piece of cloth

 What did we learn?

1. What is a thunderstorm?

2. What causes lightning?

3. What causes thunder?

Taking it further

1. Why does hail form in thunderstorms that have high clouds?

2. Why do thunderstorms usually form on hot summer days?

 **Challenge – Flash floods**

List things you can do to be safer in a severe thunderstorm.

16 Tornadoes

Swirling wind

 Supply list – Tornado in a bottle

☐ Two empty 2-liter plastic bottles

☐ Duct tape

☐ Plastic tornado tube connector
(optional but recommended)

What did we learn?

1. What causes a tornado to develop?

2. What is the difference between a funnel cloud and a tornado?

3. What is a waterspout?

4. When do most tornadoes occur in the United States?

🚀 Taking it further

1. How does the jet stream affect tornado formation?

2. Why should you take shelter during a tornado?

17 Hurricanes

Typhoons

 **Supply list – Storm word scramble**

☐ Copy of "Storm Word Scramble" worksheet

What did we learn?

1. What is a hurricane?

2. Where do most hurricanes occur?

3. What is the difference between a tropical depression, a tropical storm, and a hurricane?

Taking it further

1. Why does a hurricane dissipate once it reaches land?

2. How does warm water help create and energize a hurricane?

🧪 Storm Word Scramble

Use the clues below to help you unscramble each storm-related word or phrase found in the brackets.

1. When warm, moist air cools. _____ [ndcoesantnoi]

2. A large amount of air with uniform temperature and humidity. _____ [ira smas]

3. Where two air masses meet. _____ [nfort]

4. Air movements caused by the sun heating the ground more near the equator than at the poles.

   _____ [logabl snwdi]

5. A very high, fast-moving current of air. _____ [ejt meatrs]

6. Phenomenon caused when ions discharge energy in a cloud. _____ [glinihgtn]

7. A spiraling cloud that does not touch the ground. _____ [lufnen locdu]

8. A tornado that forms over water. _____ [treswatupo]

9. A hurricane that forms in the Pacific Ocean. _____ [ptonohy]

10. Rising sea level in front of a hurricane. _____ [msrto sgreu]

11. Equipment used by National Weather Service to predict tornadoes and hurricanes.

    _____ [poDprel rraad]

12. Person who studies the weather. _____ [mteeoorlgitso]

13. Location where 90% of hurricanes form. _____ [fciPcai cOnea]

14. Type of cloud found in thunderstorms. _____ [cuulmnimosub]

15. Instrument for indicating wind direction. _____ [iwnd scko]

18 Gathering Weather Information

What is the weather like?

Supply list – Using a psychrometer

☐ 2 nondigital thermometers

☐ Rubber band

☐ Cotton cloth

☐ Dish of water

☐ Sling psychrometer (optional)

What did we learn?

1. What does a meteorologist measure with a thermometer?

2. What is air temperature?

3. What are the two temperature scales commonly used?

4. What does a meteorologist measure with a barometer?

5. What is air pressure?

6. What does a meteorologist measure with a psychrometer?

7. What is relative humidity?

🚀 Taking it further

1. Why does a sling psychrometer give faster results than a stationary psychrometer?

2. Why do thermometers need to be kept out of direct sunlight?

19 More Weather Instruments

What else do they use?

Supply list – Making a rain gauge

☐ Jar with flat bottom

☐ Ruler

☐ Masking tape

☐ Waterproof marker

What did we learn?

1. How do meteorologists measure wind?

2. How do meteorologists measure weather at higher altitudes?

3. What sophisticated instruments do meteorologists use?

🚀 Taking it further

1. Why is it important for a meteorologist to take weather readings at higher altitudes?

2. Why might a weather satellite be useful for tracking a hurricane?

3. Why are computers necessary for weather tracking and forecasting?

20 Reporting & Analyzing Weather Information

Making it all make sense

Supply list – Analyzing weather information
☐ Copy of "Weather Station Model" worksheet

What did we learn?

1. What happens to the weather data collected at weather stations?

2. Other than from land-based weather stations, where does the National Weather Service get weather information?

3. What group of the National Weather Service generates local severe thunderstorm and flash flood warnings?

Taking it further

1. Why is it necessary for one location to collect and analyze all of the weather data across the United States?

2. Why is a standard picture or model needed for reporting weather information?

3. Why must the information in the model be converted to electrical signals before it is transmitted to the National Weather Service's computer?

Name _____   Date_____

⚗ Weather Station Model Worksheet

Using the information given in the lesson, analyze the weather station model below and answer the questions.

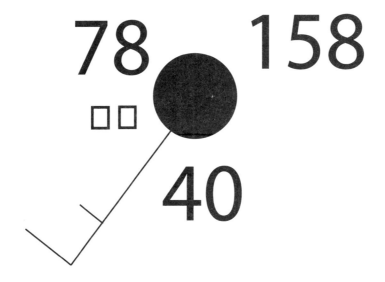

1. How much of the sky is covered with clouds? _____

2. From which direction is the wind blowing? _____

3. What is the wind speed? _____

4. What is the current temperature? _____

5. Is any precipitation falling? If so, what kind? _____

6. What is the current dew point? _____

7. What is the current air pressure? _____

21 Forecasting the Weather

Keeping people safe

Supply list – Forecasting the weather

☐ Copy of "Weather Forecasting" worksheet

☐ Newspaper, TV, or Internet weather report

Supplies for Challenge – Severe weather terminology

☐ Graph paper

☐ Colored pencils

☐ Data from "Weather Forecasting" worksheet

What did we learn?

1. How do meteorologists predict what the weather will be like?

2. What is an important function of local National Weather Service offices?

3. Other than local weather forecasts, what types of weather forecasts are generated by the NWS?

Taking it further

1. Why are weather forecasts more accurate today than they were 20 years ago?

2. Are weather forecasts always reliable?

Name _____   Date_____

🧪 Weather Forecasting Worksheet

Using the weather forecast from a local newspaper, local television news report, or the Internet, record the meteorologist's forecast for the next day's weather. Next, make your own prediction for the next day's weather and record it on the chart below. Each day, check the weather report and record the actual data, the meteorologist's predictions for the next day, and your new forecast.

| | Meteorologist's predictions | | My predictions | | Actual values | |
Date	High temp	Low temp	High temp	Low temp	High temp	Low temp

22 Weather Station: Final Project

Collecting your own data

⚗ Final Project supply list – Making a weather station

☐ Copy of "Weather Data Sheet"

☐ Clear plastic tubing

☐ Food coloring

☐ Modeling clay

☐ Waterproof marker

☐ String

☐ Empty 2-liter bottle

☐ Ruler

☐ Soda straw

☐ Duct tape

☐ Thin stick or skewer

☐ Cardboard or tagboard

☐ Weather station with an anemometer (optional)

🧠 What did we learn?

1. What does each instrument in your weather station measure?

🚀 Taking it further

1. Why might you want to have your own weather station?

2. Why might your weather readings be different from what is reported in the newspaper or on TV?

3. Did you see any relationship between air pressure and wind and rain?

4. What changes did you see in your temperature readings from day to day?

Name _____ Date _____

🔬 Weather Data Sheet

Date	High temperature	Low temperature	Air pressure (up/dn/steady)	Relative humidity	Wind speed (# of lines)	Wind direction	Clouds	Precipitation

23 Overview of the Oceans

Exploring the seas

Supply list – Labeling the oceans

☐ Copy of "World Map"

☐ World atlas

☐ Colored pencils or markers

 What did we learn?

1. What are the names of the five oceans?

2. Which ocean is the largest?

3. How much of the earth is covered by the oceans?

Taking it further

1. How do the oceans affect the weather?

2. Why do some people say there is only one ocean?

3. Why was the Indian Ocean the first ocean to have established trade routes?

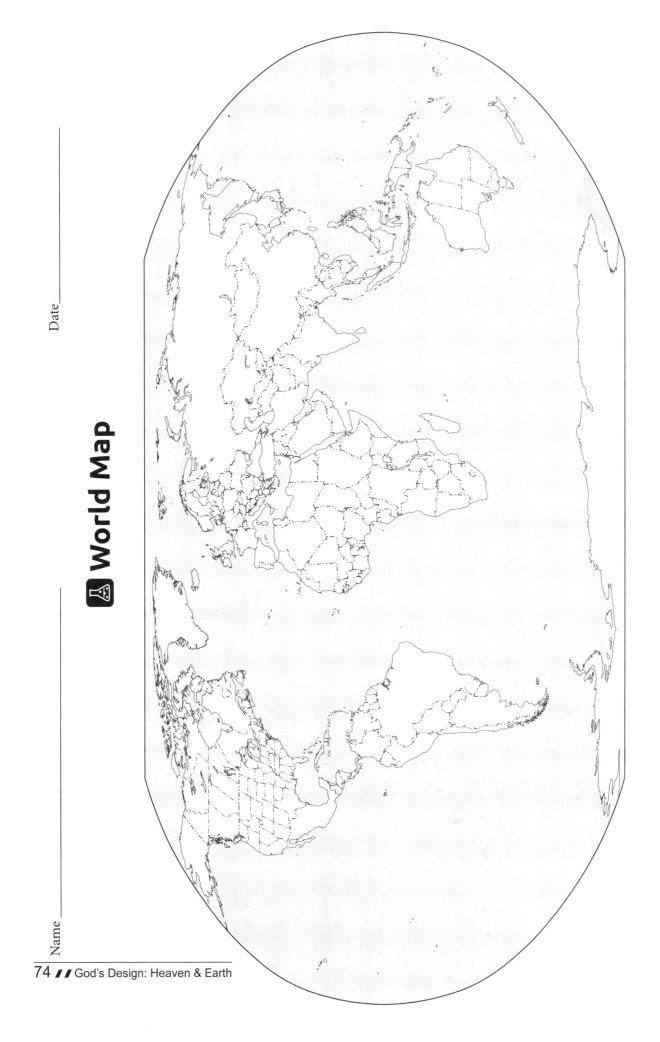

Name

Date

🔬 World Map

24 Composition of Seawater

Isn't it just water?

🧪 Supply list – Salting the ocean

☐ Dark construction paper

☐ Salt

☐ Paintbrush

☐ Water

☐ Stove

☐ Pan

🧠 What did we learn?

1. What are the main elements found in the ocean besides water?

2. How does salt get into the ocean?

3. What is one gas that is dissolved in the ocean water?

🚀 Taking it further

1. Why is there more oxygen near the surface of the ocean than in deeper parts?

2. How does the saltiness of the ocean support the idea of a young earth?

25 Ocean Currents

Moving around the world

🧪 Supply list – Observing currents

☐ Small bottle or jar

☐ Large glass bowl

☐ Red and blue food coloring

🎖 Supplies for Challenge – Surface currents

☐ "World Map" from Lesson 23

☐ Map showing the predominant surface currents

☐ Red and blue colored pencils or markers

🧠 What did we learn?

1. What is a surface ocean current?

2. What are the main causes of surface currents?

3. How fast do surface currents usually move?

4. What is a subsurface ocean current?

5. What are the main causes of subsurface currents?

🚀 Taking it further

1.   What climate changes do warm surface currents cause?

2.   What climate changes do cool surface currents cause?

3.   Why do warm surface currents move away from the equator while cooler currents move toward the equator?

26 Waves

Gently lapping the shore

🧪 Supply list – Making waves

☐ Small and large bottle

☐ String

☐ Slinky

☐ Sink or tub

🧠 What did we learn?

1. How are waves generated?

2. How far does a particular water molecule move when a wave is generated?

3. What is the crest of a wave?

4. What is the trough of a wave?

5. What are two ways to measure a wave?

🚀 Taking it further

1. Explain how a wave can move across the ocean without moving the water molecules across the ocean.

2. What kind of a path does an individual water molecule take in a wave?

3. Why does a wave get tall as it approaches the shore?

4. Why are tsunamis such dangerous waves?

27 Tides

The highs and lows of the sea

Supply list – Ocean movements

☐ Copy of "Ocean Movements Word Search"

What did we learn?

1. What is a high tide?

2. What causes the water level to change along the shore?

3. How often does a high or low tide occur each day?

Taking it further

1. Why does a spring tide only occur when there is a full moon or when there is a new moon?

2. Since the sun is so much larger than the moon, why doesn't it have a greater effect on the tides than the moon?

3. Where should you build your sandcastle if you don't want the water to knock it down?

🧪 Ocean Movements Word Search

Find the following words in the puzzle below. Words may be horizontal, vertical, or diagonal, including backward.

breaker	friction	neap	tsunami
crest	gravity	subsurface	rip
current	high	tide	wavelength
density	low	trough	wind

I	P	M	C	B	E	I	Y	D	N	E	A	P	X	Z
C	B	R	G	R	A	I	F	C	E	K	P	L	U	Y
U	O	E	R	I	B	L	I	M	A	N	U	S	T	W
R	F	W	A	V	E	L	E	N	G	T	H	T	D	Q
R	H	F	V	B	R	E	A	K	E	R	F	I	E	E
E	K	L	I	N	J	I	E	Y	L	O	W	W	S	R
N	N	E	T	L	Y	R	E	T	V	U	C	S	C	E
T	D	E	Y	S	W	H	R	I	K	G	J	G	R	V
X	T	Z	Y	W	G	O	U	S	N	H	V	F	E	L
M	N	H	T	I	D	E	L	N	F	T	V	N	S	O
V	C	K	H	N	I	H	U	E	I	R	I	P	T	B
R	E	D	S	D	H	I	J	D	K	L	D	E	V	D
C	A	F	E	H	U	F	R	I	C	T	I	O	N	N
I	D	I	E	C	A	F	R	U	S	B	U	S	U	X
V	G	I	J	K	Y	T	S	T	R	U	N	F	Q	O

28 Wave Erosion

Wearing down the shore

Supply list – Observing erosion

☐ Paint roller pan

☐ Sand

☐ Empty plastic bottle

Supplies for Challenge – Erosional landforms

☐ Copy of "Erosional Land Formations" worksheet

What did we learn?

1. What causes erosion along a beach?

2. What are some problems that can arise from wave erosion?

3. What features have been formed along the shore by the erosion from waves?

Taking it further

1. Why don't shores completely erode if water is constantly pulling sand away from them?

2. How can you protect your building from the damaging effects of tsunamis and other storm-generated waves?

🎖 Erosional Land Formations

Label the pictures of the land formations below, using the definitions in the lesson to identify them.

1.

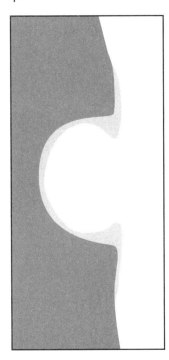

2.

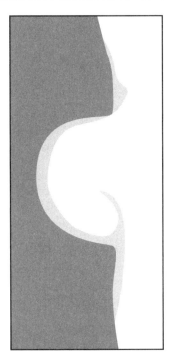

3.

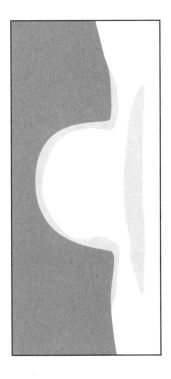

4.

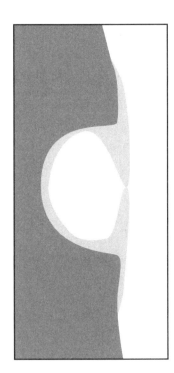

29 Energy from the Ocean

Making it work for us

 **Supply list – Read about the ocean**

☐ *The Magic School Bus on the Ocean Floor* by Joanna Cole

Supplies for Challenge – Ocean energy research

☐ Research materials on ocean energy methods

What did we learn?

1. What are three ways that people are using the ocean to generate electricity?

Taking it further

1. Why are tidal barrages used infrequently?

2. Why do heat exchangers have to be built near the equator?

3. Scientists hope to use the warm tropical waters to generate electricity. What natural weather phenomenon is fueled by these warm tropical waters?

30 Sea Exploration

Exploring the depths

 **Supply list – Practice diving**

☐ Deck of playing cards

What did we learn?

1. What invention in the 1940s allowed divers to more freely explore the ocean?

2. How do oceanographers study the ocean today?

3. What special equipment do submersibles have?

🚀 Taking it further

1. Why does a submersible or ROV need headlights?

2. Why can't scuba divers go very deep in the ocean?

3. How are submersibles similar to spacecraft?

31 Geography of the Ocean Floor

Mountains and valleys

 Supply list – Seeing the ocean floor

☐ Empty aquarium or other glass case

☐ Modeling clay

Supplies for Challenge – Trenches & ridges

☐ "World Map" from Lesson 23

What did we learn?

1. What are the three areas of the ocean floor?

2. What are some features of the abyssal plain?

3. What is a guyot?

1. What part of the ocean floor is most difficult to observe?

2. What do you think is the most likely cause of seamounts?

32 Ocean Zones

Visiting the different levels

🧪 Supply list – Ocean zones worksheet

☐ Copy of "Ocean Zones" worksheet

☐ Crayons or colored pencils

🏅 Supplies for Challenge – Sea creature report

☐ Research materials on various sea creatures

🧠 What did we learn?

1. What are the five ocean zones?

2. What zone has the most life?

3. Where is the sunlit zone located?

🚀 Taking it further

1. Why is algae and plant life found in the sunlit zone?

2. Why are so few animals found in the very deepest parts of the ocean?

🧪 Ocean Zones Worksheet

Label each zone in the chart below and then draw pictures of the plants and animals that might be found in each zone. Use the words below to help you label the chart.

Trench   Sunlit zone   Midnight zone   Abyss   Twilight zone

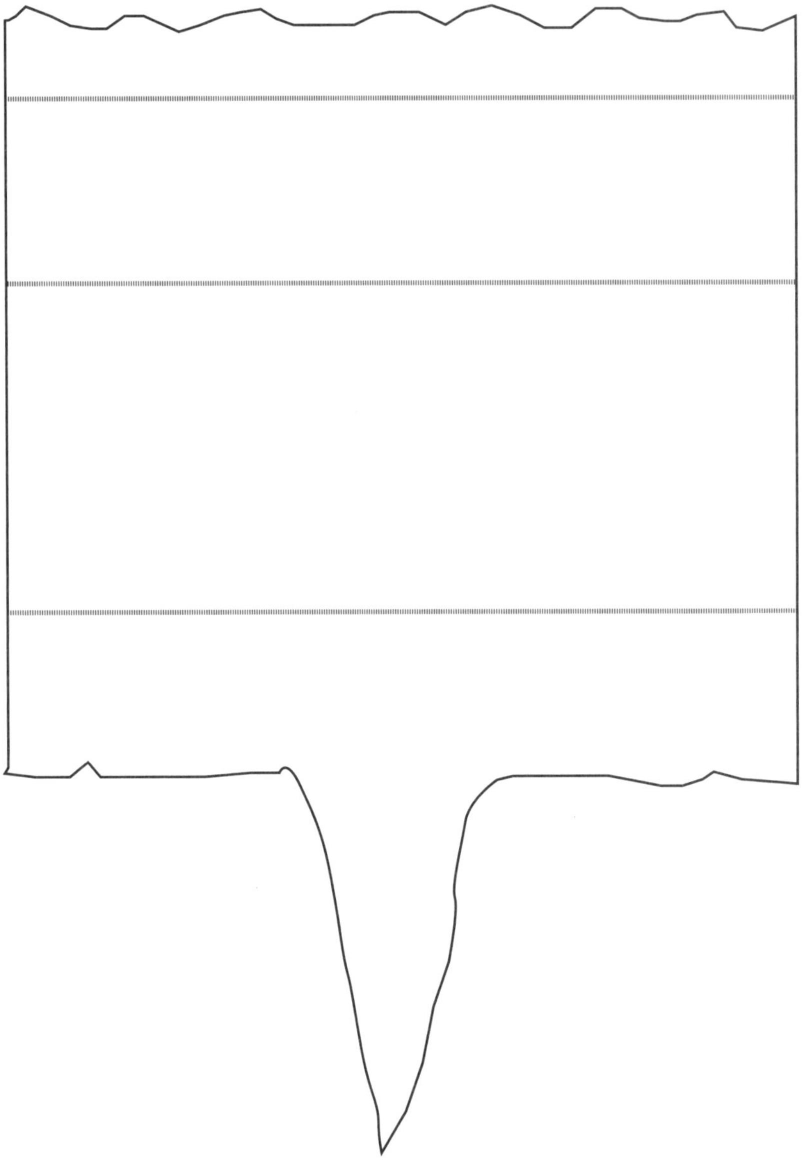

1. _____

2. _____

3. _____

4. _____

5. _____

33 Vents & Smokers

Underwater volcanoes?

 Supply list – Discovering new life forms

☐ Paper

☐ Colored pencils or markers

What did we learn?

1. What is a deep-sea vent?

2. What provides the food source for the animals living near these vents?

🚀 Taking it further

1. Why were scientists so surprised to find an ecosystem thriving near the deep-sea vents?

2. Why can the water stay so hot near the vents without turning to steam?

34 Coral Reefs

Animal-made islands

 Supply list – Coral models

☐ Modeling clay

Supplies for Challenge – How old are coral reefs?

☐ Research materials on the Great Barrier Reef

What did we learn?

1. What is a coral?

2. What is a coral reef?

3. What are the three types of coral reefs?

🚀 Taking it further

1. Why are coral reefs only found in relatively shallow ocean water?

2. Why might a coral reef be a hazard to ships?

3. What could happen to a coral reef if the water became cloudy or too warm for the algae to survive?

35 Conclusion

Appreciating our weather and water

🔬 Supply list – Reflecting on God's creation
☐ Bible

Astronomy Worksheets

for Use with

Our Universe
(*God's Design: Heaven & Earth*)

1 Introduction to Astronomy

Study of space

 Supply list – God's purpose

☐ Bible

☐ Copy of "God's Purpose for the Universe" worksheet

Supplies for Challenge – Knowledge of the stars

☐ Copy of "Knowledge of the Stars" worksheet

What did we learn?

1. What is astronomy?

2. Why should we want to study astronomy?

Taking it further

1. What is one thing you really want to learn during this study?

2. Write your question or questions on a piece of paper and save it to make sure you find the answers by the end of the book.

🧪 God's Purpose For the Universe Worksheet

Use your Bible to help answer the following riddles about the universe. The references given below should help you.

1. I was designed to rule the day: _____ (Genesis 1:14–19)

2. I was designed to rule the night: _____ (Genesis 1:14–19)

3. We are the times that are to be marked by the movement of the sun, moon, and stars:

    _____ (Genesis 1:14–19)

4. Besides marking times, I am another reason why the sun, moon, and stars were made:

    _____ (Genesis 1:14–19)

5. We were made by God's hands and this is what will eventually happen to us:

    _____ (Psalm 102:25–26)

6. This is higher than me: _____ (Isaiah 55:8–9)

7. I am what you will see in the heavens in the last days:

    _____ (Joel 2:28–32)

8. I stood still for this long until Joshua and the Israelites defeated their enemies:

    _____(Joshua 10:12–15)

Name _____   Date_____

🎖 Knowledge of the Stars Worksheet

1. What is the nearest star to the earth?_____

2. What are the two main elements in stars? _____ and

   _____

3. What is the name of the galaxy that we live in?_____

4. What is special about Polaris, the North Star?_____

5. What unit of distance is used to measure items in space?_____

6. What name describes when one celestial body blocks the light from another?

   _____

7. What force holds the planets in their places? _____

8. Name three items found in space besides stars, moons, and planets.

   _____

9. Name two scientists important to our understanding of astronomy.

   _____

10. Approximately how long does it take for light to travel from the sun to the earth?

    _____

2 Space Models

What's really out there?

Supply list – Gravitational pull

☐ Book

☐ Piece of paper

☐ Ping-pong ball

☐ Golf ball

Supplies for Challenge – Research the scientists

☐ Research materials on past scientists

What did we learn?

1. What are the two major models that have been used to describe the arrangement of the solar system?

2. What was the main idea of the geocentric model?

3. What is the main idea of the heliocentric model?

4. What force holds all of the planets in orbit around the sun?

🚀 Taking it further

1. Which exerts the most gravitational pull, the earth or the sun?

2. If the sun has a stronger gravitational pull, then why aren't objects pulled off of the earth toward the sun?

3 The Earth's Movement

Rotating and revolving

🧪 Supply list – Demonstrating movement

☐ Flashlight

☐ Basketball or volleyball

☐ Masking tape

🏅 Supplies for Challenge – Foucault pendulum

☐ Copy of "Clock" pattern

☐ Tripod

☐ Thread

☐ Tape

☐ Needle

☐ Modeling clay

☐ Turntable, swivel chair or stool, etc.

🧠 What did we learn?

1. What are the two different types of motion that the earth experiences?

2. What observations can we make that are the result of the rotation of the earth on its axis?

3. What observations can we make that are the result of the revolution of the earth around the sun?

4. What is a solstice?

5.   What is an equinox?

⚀ Taking it further

1.   What are the advantages of the earth being tilted on its axis as it revolves around the sun?

2.   One argument against Copernicus's theory was that if the earth were moving, flying birds would be left behind. Why don't the birds get left behind as the earth moves through space?

⚀ Challenge questions – Foucault pendulum

1.   What forces are affecting the pendulum?

2.   Why does the pendulum eventually stop moving?

3.   How does a Foucault pendulum keep moving for hours or days at a time without stopping?

Name _____   Date _____

🎖 Clock

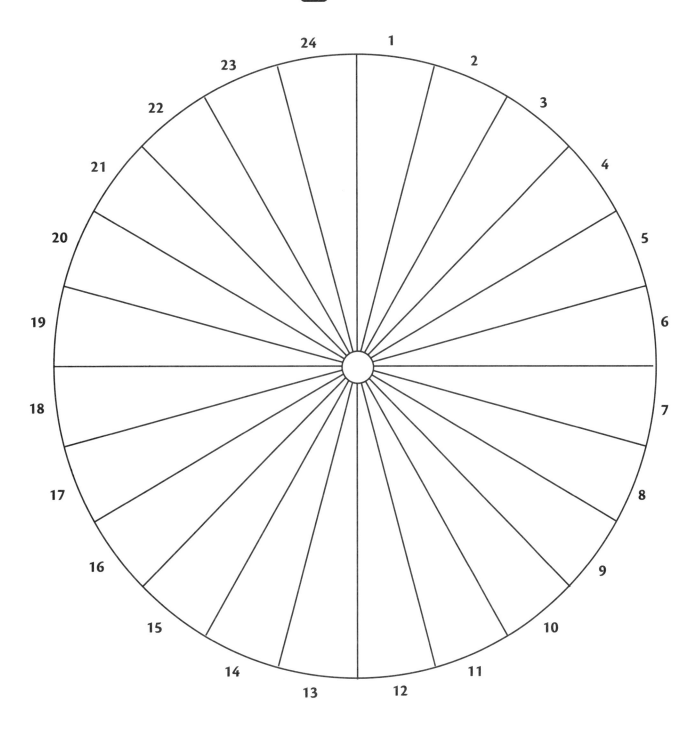

 **Tools for Studying Space**

Do I need more than my eyes?

🧪 Supply list – Refraction & reflection

☐ Mirror

☐ Magnifying glass

☐ Flashlight

☐ Access to a telescope (optional)

🎖 Supplies for Challenge – Telescope advances

☐ Sheet of paper

☐ Black marker

☐ Car

🧠 What did we learn?

1. What are the three main types of telescopes?

2. What was one disadvantage of the early refracting telescope?

3. How did Newton avoid this problem?

Taking it further

1. Why do you think scientists wanted to put a telescope in space?

2. What kinds of things can we learn from using optical telescopes?

3. What kinds of things can we learn from radio telescopes?

5 Overview of the Universe

How big is it?

 **Supply list – Observing the night sky**

☐ Star chart

☐ Clear night sky

What did we learn?

1. What is our solar system?

2. Our solar system is part of which galaxy?

3. How big is the universe?

Taking it further

1. Why do you think our galaxy is called the Milky Way?

2. Why do you need star charts that are different for different times of the year?

3. Why do you need star charts that are different for different times of the night?

🏅 Challenge questions – Locating stars

1. Explain how a star map is similar to a map of the globe.

2. What units are used to measure declination and ascension?

3. How does an astronomer define a constellation differently than most people?

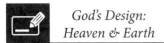

Stars

Twinkle, twinkle little star

🧪 Supply list – Simulating starlight

☐ Copy of "Starlight" worksheet

☐ Ruler and a yardstick

☐ 2 flashlights (one brighter than the other or with different sizes of lenses)

🎖 Supplies for Challenge – Origin of stars

☐ Calculator

🧠 What did we learn?

1. What is the unit of distance used to measure how far away something is in space?

2. How far is a light-year?

3. What does the color of a star tell us about that star?

🚀 Taking it further

1. What causes stars to appear to move in the sky?

2. How can we determine if a star's absolute distance from the earth is actually changing over time?

3. Why is brightness not a good indicator of the distance of a star from the earth?

Name _____   Date_____

🧪 Starlight Worksheet

Part 1

Have one person hold a flashlight 1 foot from the wall and shine the beam on the wall while a second person measures the diameter (length across) of the light beam. Record your observations on the chart below. Repeat with the flashlight 2 feet and 3 feet from the wall.

Distance of flashlight from the wall	Diameter of light beam on the wall	Brightness of the light beam on the wall (brightest to dimmest)
1 Foot		
2 Feet		
3 Feet		

1. What happened to the light beam as the flashlight was moved farther from the wall?

   _____

2. How would two identical stars appear to someone on earth if one was much farther away?

   _____

Part 2

Have two people hold two different flashlights 1 foot from the wall and shine them on the wall. Record your observations below:

Flashlight 1		Flashlight 2	
Diameter of beam on wall	Brightness of beam (brighter or dimmer)	Diameter of beam on wall	Brightness of beam (brighter or dimmer)

3. Have the person with the brightest flashlight move away from the wall until the light beams are approximately the same diameter and brightness.

   Record this distance: _____

4. Why could two stars with the same apparent brightness be different distances from the earth?

   _____

7 Heavenly Bodies

More than just stars

 **Supply list – Making a nebula**

☐ Flashlight

☐ Pencil

What did we learn?

1. What is a cluster of stars?

2. What is a galaxy?

3. Explain the difference between a nova, a supernova, and a neutron star.

🚀 Taking it further

1. How can a star appear to become brighter and dimmer on a regular basis?

2. Why does starlight from millions of light-years away not prove that the earth is old?

8 Asteroids

Minor planets

 Supply list – Naming asteroids

☐ Paper and pencil

Supplies for Challenge – Trojan asteroids

☐ Research materials for the Trojan War

☐ Paper and pencil

What did we learn?

1. What is an asteroid?

2. Where are most asteroids in our solar system located?

3. What is another name for asteroids?

1.   What is the chance that an asteroid will hit the earth?

9 Comets

Look at that tail!

🧪 Supply list – Comet model

☐ Small Styrofoam™ ball

☐ Tagboard/poster board

☐ Glue

☐ Glitter

🧠 What did we learn?

1. What is a comet?

2. Who was the first person to accurately predict the orbit of comets?

3. What are the two main parts of a comet?

🚀 Taking it further

1. Why does a comet's tail always point away from the sun?

2. Why doesn't a comet have a tail when it is far from the sun?

3. When will Halley's Comet next appear?

Challenge – God created comets

Comets can be powerful tools to support the Bible. Explain how what you have learned about comets can support each of the following Scriptures:

1. "Lift up your eyes to the heavens, And look on the earth beneath. For the heavens will vanish away like smoke, The earth will grow old like a garment, And those who dwell in it will die in like manner; But My salvation will be forever, And My righteousness will not be abolished." —Isaiah 51:6

2. Then God said, "Let there be lights in the firmament of the heavens to divide the day from the night; and let them be for signs and seasons, and for days and years." —Genesis 1:14

3. Thus says the LORD: "Do not learn the way of the Gentiles; Do not be dismayed at the signs of heaven, For the Gentiles are dismayed at them." —Jeremiah 10:2

4. "In the beginning was the Word, and the Word was with God, and the Word was God. He was in the beginning with God. All things were made through Him, and without Him nothing was made that was made." —John 1:1–3

10 Meteors

Shooting stars

🧪 Supply list – The sky is falling

☐ Pie pan

☐ Salt

☐ Flour

☐ Marble

☐ Toys

☐ Golf ball

🧠 What did we learn?

1. What is the difference between a meteoroid, meteor, and meteorite?

2. When is the best time to watch for meteors?

🚀 Taking it further

1. Space dust (extremely small meteorites) is constantly falling on the earth. If this has been going on for billions of years, what would you expect to find on the earth and in the oceans?

2. Have we discovered these things?

11 Overview of Our Solar System

Revolving around the sun

 Supply list – Learning the names of the planets

☐ A willingness to sing

Supplies for Challenge – Laws of planetary motion

☐ Cardboard

☐ String

☐ 2 thumb tacks

☐ Piece of paper

☐ Tape

☐ Pencil

What did we learn?

1. Name the eight planets in our solar system.

2. Name two dwarf planets.

3. Which planets can support life?

🚀 Taking it further

1. What are the major differences between the inner and outer planets?

2. Why are the gas planets called Jovian planets?

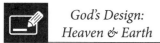

12 Our Sun

The center of our solar system

🧪 Supply list – Viewing sunlight

☐ Pie pan

☐ Small mirror

☐ Prism (optional)

🏅 Supplies for Challenge – Diameter of the sun

☐ Copy of "Sun Measurement" worksheet

☐ 2 index cards

☐ Needle

☐ Meter stick

☐ Ruler

☐ Tape

☐ Calculator

🧠 What did we learn?

1. What are the main elements found in the sun?

2. What colors are found in sunlight?

🚀 Taking it further

1. Why is the sun so important to us?

2. How does energy get from the sun to the earth?

🎖 Sun Measurement Worksheet

Use a pinhole projector to make the following measurements.

	Diameter of image
Trial 1	
Trial 2	
Trial 3	
Average	

Using the distance between the cards and the average diameter above, you can now calculate the diameter of the sun. We know from geometry that the ratios of the sides of two similar triangles are equal so we know that the following equation is true.

$$\frac{\text{Diameter of the sun}}{\text{Distance of the earth to sun}} = \frac{\text{Diameter of the image}}{\text{Distance from projector to image}}$$

If we solve for the diameter of the sun we get:

$$\text{Diameter of the sun} = \text{Distance of earth to sun} \ \times \ \frac{\text{Diameter of the image}}{\text{Distance from projector to image}}$$

The distance from the earth to the sun is approximately 93,000,000 miles (150,000,000 km).

If you are using a yard stick, plug your average measurement into this equation:

$$\text{Diameter of the sun} = 93,000,000 \text{ miles} \ \times \ \frac{\text{Diameter of the image (inches)}}{36 \text{ inches}}$$

If you are using a meter stick, plug your average measurement into this equation:

$$\text{Diameter of the sun} = 150,000,000 \text{ km} \ \times \ \frac{\text{Diameter of the image (mm)}}{1,000 \text{ mm}}$$

Diameter of the sun = _____

1. The actual diameter of the sun is approximately 868,000 miles (1,400,000 km). What would account for the differences in your caculated value versus the known value?

    _____

2. How does the diameter of the sun compare with the diameter of the earth?

    _____

13 Structure of the Sun

What is it like on the inside?

 Supply list – Tracking the earth's movement

☐ Sidewalk chalk

Note: It is most effective if you start this project in the morning.

What did we learn?

1. What are the two parts of the sun's atmosphere?

2. What is a sunspot?

3. Are sunspots stationary?

4. What do scientists believe are the three parts of the sun's interior?

🚀 Taking it further

1. What is the hottest part of the sun?

2. What causes the aurora borealis or northern lights?

3. When do you think scientists study the sun's corona?

14 Solar Eclipse

Where did it go?

🧪 Supply list – Making an eclipse

☐ Flashlight

☐ Small ball (e.g., tennis ball)

☐ Large ball (e.g., basketball or volleyball)

🎖 Supplies for Challenge – Total solar eclipse

☐ Research materials on past and future lunar and solar eclipses

🧠 What did we learn?

1. What is an eclipse?

2. What is the difference between a partial and a total eclipse?

3. How often do solar eclipses occur?

1. Why do you think plants and animals start preparing for nightfall during an eclipse?

2. Why can a total eclipse only be seen in a small area on the earth?

3. How can the moon block out the entire sun when the sun is 400 times bigger than the moon?

15 Solar Energy

Can it meet our energy needs?

🧪 Supply list – Solar energy

☐ Copy of "Solar Energy" worksheet

☐ Black, white, and green construction paper

☐ 2 clear glasses

☐ 2 thermometers

☐ Ice cubes

☐ Tape

☐ Baking sheet

🏅 Supplies for Challenge – Solar energy

☐ Hardback book

☐ Flashlight

☐ Clipboard

☐ Piece of paper

☐ Pencil

🧠 What did we learn?

1. What is solar energy?

2. What are the two ways that solar energy is used today?

🚀 Taking it further

1. Why is solar energy a good alternative to fossil fuels?

2. Why are the insides of solar collectors painted black?

3. What are some of the advantages of using solar cells in outer space?

🎖 Challenge questions – Solar energy

1. Is the new pattern bigger or smaller than the first pattern?

2. Based on what you just learned, where would be the best location for a solar energy power plant?

Name _____   Date_____

🧪 Solar Energy Worksheet

Activity 1: What color should solar collectors be painted? To test which color absorbs the most heat, set up the following experiment.

Place a piece of black paper, a piece of green paper, and a piece of white paper side by side on a baking sheet. Place an ice cube on each sheet of paper. Set the baking sheet in a sunny location. Record the time you set the sheet in the sun as the starting time and the time the ice was completely melted as the ending time on the chart below.

Color of paper	Starting time	Ending time	Time to melt ice
Black			
Green			
White			

1. On which color of paper did the ice melt the fastest? _____

2. On which color of paper did the ice melt the slowest? _____

Activity 2: To demonstrate how the sun heats water in a solar collector, set up the following experiment.

Fill two clear glasses with water. Wrap black paper around one glass and tape it in place. Place both glasses side by side in a sunny location. Write down the starting time of your experiment. Use a thermometer to measure the temperature of the water in each glass and record it on the chart below. Repeat the temperature measurement every 5 minutes for 20 minutes and record the results on the chart below.

Time	Temperature in clear glass	Temperature in black glass

3. Which glass had the higher temperature after 20 minutes? _____

4. Solar collectors are designed to absorb as much heat energy as possible. What color would you use to paint a solar collector?

_____

16 Our Moon

Is it made of green cheese?

Supply list – Reflected light

☐ Hand mirror

☐ Flashlight

Supplies for Challenge – Surface of the moon

☐ Binoculars or telescope (if available)

What did we learn?

1. Why does the moon shine?

2. What causes the dark spots on the surface of the moon?

🚀 Taking it further

1.   Why does the size of our moon show God's provision for man?

2.   Why is gravity much less on the moon than on the earth?

3.   Why doesn't the surface of the earth have as many craters as the surface of the moon?

17 Motion & Phases of the Moon

There's a full moon tonight

🧪 Supply list – Moon phases

☐ Copy of "Identifying Phases of the Moon" worksheet

🎖 Supplies for Challenge – Observing the moon

☐ Copy of "Observing the Phases of the Moon" worksheet

🧠 What did we learn?

1. What causes the phases of the moon?

2. Why does the same side of the moon always face the earth?

3. What causes a lunar eclipse?

4. From the perspective of space, how long does it take for the moon to complete its cycle around the earth?

🚀 Taking it further

1. Why doesn't a lunar eclipse occur every month?

2. What is the difference between a waxing crescent and a waning crescent?

🎖 Challenge questions – Observing the moon

1. When is the light side of the moon the same as the near side of the moon?

2. When is the dark side of the moon the same as the near side of the moon?

Name _____   Date_____

🧪 Identifying Phases of the Moon Worksheet

Label each phase of the moon. Use the words below.

Full moon	Waxing crescent	First quarter	Waxing gibbous
New moon	Waning crescent	Last quarter	Waning gibbous

A little trick to help you remember whether a moon is waxing (getting bigger) or waning (getting smaller) is to mentally draw a line between the dark and light parts of the moon. If the lighted part forms a lower case *b* the moon is being "born" or waxing. If the lighted part forms a lower case *d* the moon is "dying" or waning.

1._____   2._____   3._____   4._____

5._____   6._____   7._____   8._____

◉ Observing the Phases of the Moon Worksheet

○ ○ ○ ○ ○ ○

Date: _____ _____ _____ _____ _____ _____

Moon rise: _____ _____ _____ _____ _____ _____

Moon set: _____ _____ _____ _____ _____ _____

○ ○ ○ ○ ○ ○

Date: _____ _____ _____ _____ _____ _____

Moon rise: _____ _____ _____ _____ _____ _____

Moon set: _____ _____ _____ _____ _____ _____

○ ○ ○ ○ ○ ○

Date: _____ _____ _____ _____ _____ _____

Moon rise: _____ _____ _____ _____ _____ _____

Moon set: _____ _____ _____ _____ _____ _____

○ ○ ○ ○ ○ ○

Date: _____ _____ _____ _____ _____ _____

Moon rise: _____ _____ _____ _____ _____ _____

Moon set: _____ _____ _____ _____ _____ _____

○ ○ ○ ○ ○

Date: _____ _____ _____ _____ _____

Moon rise: _____ _____ _____ _____ _____

Moon set: _____

18 Origin of the Moon

Where did it come from?

 **Supply list – Spinning bodies**

☐ 2 tops (spinning toys)

☐ Masking tape

Supplies for Challenge – Origin of the moon

☐ Bible

What did we learn?

1. What are four secular theories for the origin of the moon?

2. Which of these theories is most likely to be true?

3. What does the Bible say about the origin of the moon?

Taking it further

1. What are the main difficulties with the Capture Theory?

2. Why do you think scientists come up with unworkable ideas for the moon's origin?

⊛ Challenge – Origin of the moon

Read the following verses and discuss what each says about the origin of the moon.

Genesis 1:14–19

Psalm 8:3–4

Psalm 33:6

Psalm 74:16

Psalm 136:3–9

Jeremiah 31:35

It is clear from the Bible that no naturalistic explanation will adequately explain the moon's origin because its creation was supernatural.

19 Mercury

Closest planet to the sun

🧪 Supply list – Atmosphere test

☐ Towel

☐ Hair dryer

☐ Ice

🏅 Supplies for Challenge – Mercury probe

☐ 2 index cards

☐ Flashlight

☐ 2 clear plastic cups

☐ Magnifying glass

☐ Tape

☐ Water

☐ Milk

☐ Crayons or markers

☐ Box or stack of books

🧠 What did we learn?

1. How do Mercury's revolution around the sun and rotation on its axis compare to that of Earth?

2. What is the surface of Mercury like?

🚀 Taking it further

1.   How does a lack of atmosphere affect the conditions on Mercury?

20 Venus

The second planet

Supply list – The greenhouse effect

☐ Copy of "Greenhouse Effect" worksheet

☐ Shoebox

☐ Plastic wrap

☐ Aluminum foil

☐ Tape

☐ Thermometer

☐ Scissors

Supplies for Challenge – Surface mapping

☐ Shoebox

☐ Modeling clay

☐ Graph paper

☐ Ruler

☐ String

☐ Metal washer

☐ Tape

What did we learn?

1. Where is Venus's orbit with respect to the sun and the other planets?

2. What makes Venus so bright in the sky?

3. What is a nickname for Venus?

4. How many moons does Venus have?

🚀 Taking it further

1. Even though Venus has an atmosphere, why can't life exist there?

2. Why doesn't the earth's atmosphere keep our planet too hot?

Name _____   Date_____

🧪 Greenhouse Effect Worksheet

Step 1

Line the inside of a shoebox with aluminum foil. Be sure that all surfaces are covered. Cut a small hole in the side of the box just big enough to slide a thermometer through. Slide a thermometer inside the shoebox so the tip is about in the center of the box. Allow it to stay in the shoebox for two minutes then slide it out and record the temperature on the chart below as the initial reading.

Step 2

Slide the thermometer back into the box. Completely cover the opening of the shoebox with plastic wrap. Tape it in place around the edges. Place the box in a window where the sun will shine on the plastic-covered opening. Read the temperature every five minutes and record your readings for 15 minutes.

Time	Temperature
Initial reading: 0 minutes	
5 minutes	
10 minutes	
15 minutes	

1. What did you observe about the temperature in the box when it was covered with plastic wrap?

    _____

2. Why did the temperature do this?

    _____

3. What do you think the temperature would be inside the box if you left it in the sun for several hours?

    _____

What you observed is called the greenhouse effect. Greenhouses are built out of material that traps heat from the sun, keeping the greenhouse warm enough for plants to grow even in the winter. Greenhouses often need fans in the summer to keep them from getting too hot. Venus has an atmosphere that traps the heat but does not have any way to cool the planet, making it the hottest planet in the solar system.

21 Earth

Designed for life

Supply list – Earth model

☐ 1 orange per child

☐ Markers

☐ Globe

☐ World map

Supplies for Challenge – Why is the sky blue?

☐ 2 clear cups

☐ Water

☐ Milk

☐ Flashlight

What did we learn?

1. What are some features of our planet that make it uniquely able to support life?

2. What name is given to the period of time it takes for Earth's revolution around the sun?

3. What name is given to the length of Earth's rotation on its axis?

4.   On average, how far is Earth from the sun?

🚀 Taking it further

1.   What are some possible reasons why large amounts of water are found on Earth but not on other planets?

2.   Why is it important that Earth is a terrestrial planet?

22 Mars

The red planet

🧪 Supply list – Experimenting with polar ice caps

☐ Empty aquarium or other glass case

☐ Gloves

☐ Matches or lighter

☐ Cup of water

☐ Candle

☐ Dry ice (**Note:** Dry ice must be obtained shortly before it is needed and must be handled by an adult with gloves.)

🎖 Supplies for Challenge – Mars probe

☐ Research materials on Mars space probes

🧠 What did we learn?

1. Why is Mars called a superior planet?

2. Why is Mars called the red planet?

3. How many moons does Mars have?

🚀 Taking it further

1. What causes the dust storms on Mars?

2. Why doesn't the wind on Earth cause giant dust storms like the wind on Mars?

3. How would your weight on Mars compare to your weight on Mercury?

🧪 Experimenting with polar ice caps

1. What was the "smoke" coming off of the dry ice?

2. Why did the candle flame go out?

3. Why did the water in the cup "boil"?

23 Jupiter

The gas giant

Supply list – The giant planet

☐ 2 cereal bowls

☐ Marbles (enough to fill both bowls)

Supplies for Challenge – Great red spot

☐ Clear cup

☐ Water

☐ Tea bag

☐ Pencil

What did we learn?

1. What are some major differences between Jupiter and the inner planets?

2. What is the Great Red Spot?

🚀 Taking it Further

1. Why does Jupiter bulge more in the middle than Earth does?

2. Why can't life exist on Jupiter?

3. Why are space probes necessary for exploring other planets?

24 Saturn

Surrounded by beautiful rings

 **No Supplies**

 **What did we learn?**

1. Who first saw Saturn's rings?

2. What are Saturn's rings made of?

3. What makes Titan unique among moons?

🚀 Taking it further

1. Why did astronomers believe that Saturn had only a few rings before the *Voyager* space probe explored Saturn?

2. Both Titan and Earth have a mostly nitrogen atmosphere. What important differences exist between these two worlds that make Earth able to support life but Titan unable to?

25 Uranus

Seventh planet from the sun

Supply list – Rotations & revolutions

☐ Ping-pong ball

☐ Paint (two colors)

☐ Basketball, volleyball, or other larger ball

Supplies for Challenge – Tilt and rotation

☐ Modeling clay

☐ 8 pencils

☐ Protractor

☐ Index cards

What did we learn?

1. What makes Uranus unusual compared to the other planets?

2. How have rings been discovered around Uranus?

🚀 Taking it further

1. How can we learn more about Uranus?

2. Why is Uranus such a cold planet?

26 Neptune

Last of the gas giants

🧪 Supply list – Reflection of colored light

☐ Flashlight

☐ 3 clear plastic or glass cups

☐ Red and blue food coloring

🎖 Supplies for Challenge – Centripetal force

☐ String

☐ Metal washer

🧠 What did we learn?

1. What similarities are there between Uranus and Neptune?

2. What are two possible explanations for the Great Dark Spot?

🚀 Taking it further

1. Explain how Neptune was discovered.

2. What affects the color of a planet?

🎖 Challenge questions – Centripetal force

1. Were you able to spin the washer as slowly after you shortened the string?

2. How does the pressure between your hand and the string compare when the string is short and when the string is long?

27 Pluto & Eris

Plutoids

Supply list – How much do I weigh?

☐ Copy of "How Much Do I Weigh?" worksheet

☐ Calculator

☐ Bathroom scale

What did we learn?

1. What discovery was originally considered to be the ninth planet?

2. How does the gravity on Pluto compare to the gravity on Earth?

3. Is Pluto always farther away from the sun than Neptune?

4. What is unique about how Charon orbits Pluto?

Taking it further

1. Why did it take so long to discover Pluto?

2. Why is Pluto no longer considered to be a planet?

3. What alternate classification was given to Pluto in 2006?

🧪 How Much Do I Weigh? Worksheet

Your weight is determined by two factors: the amount of mass in your body and how strongly gravity pulls down on you. Because the gravitational pull differs from planet to planet, your weight will be different on each planet. Of course, you can't visit other planets and weigh yourself, but you can calculate what your weight would be on each one.

First, step on a bathroom scale and find your weight on earth. Record this amount below.

Weight on earth = _____ pounds

If your scale measures your weight in kilograms, you need to convert to pounds (1 kg = 2.2 pounds). Although in everyday usage kilograms are often used to measure weight, scientifically a kilogram is a measure of mass, which is how much of something there is and your mass does not change even if the gravitational pull changes.

The chart below shows the gravitational pull on the other planets (and plutoid) compared to the gravitational pull on earth.

Use the following formula:

Weight on other planet = weight on earth x gravitational pull

For example if your weight on earth is 80 pounds, then your weight on Mercury would be

80 pounds x 0.38 = 30.4 pounds.

Planet	Gravitational pull	My weight
Mercury	0.38	
Venus	0.91	
Earth	1.0	
Mars	0.38	
Jupiter	2.64	
Saturn	1.13	
Uranus	1.17	
Neptune	1.19	
Pluto	0.08	

28 NASA

The National Aeronautics and Space Administration

🧪 Supply list – Escape velocity

☐ Tagboard/poster board

☐ Steel BBs

☐ Magnet

☐ Plastic lid or dish

☐ Several books

☐ Tape

🧠 What did we learn?

1. What is NASA?

2. When was NASA formed?

3. What was one of NASA's first tasks?

4. List at least three different types of projects that a person at NASA could work on.

🚀 Taking it further

1. How does NASA help people who are not interested in space exploration?

2. How might an evolutionary worldview affect NASA's work?

🏅 Challenge questions – NACA

1. What was NACA?

2. What was its original purpose?

3. What were some of the major contributions to aeronautics that were made by NACA?

29 Space Exploration

Seeing what's out there

🧪 Supply list – Space satellite models

☐ Styrofoam™ balls

☐ Toothpicks

☐ Aluminum foil

☐ Modeling clay

☐ Tagboard/poster board

☐ Model rocket and launch pad (optional)

🎖 Supplies for Challenge – Commercial space flights

☐ Drawing materials

🧠 What did we learn?

1. Who were the first people to talk about going into space?

2. Who is considered the father of modern rocketry?

3. What major event sparked interest in the development of the rocket for space travel?

4. Who was one of the primary developers of rockets in the United States after World War II?

5. What was the first man-made object to orbit the earth?

6. Who was the first man in space?

7. Who was the first American in space?

8. Who was the first American to orbit the earth?

9. Who was the first man to walk on the moon?

🚀 Taking it further

1. Why are satellites an important part of space exploration?

2. Why are space probes an important part of space exploration?

30 Apollo Program

First flight to the moon

🧪 Supply list – Two-stage rocket

☐ String (enough to reach across a room)

☐ 2 balloons

☐ 2 straws

☐ Tape

🧠 What did we learn?

1. What was the name of the NASA program whose goal was to put a man on the moon?

2. What are the three modules in the Apollo spacecraft?

3. What were the two parts of the lunar module designed to do?

4. What was the name of the three-stage rocket used with the Apollo spacecraft?

🚀 Taking it further

1. What is the advantage of a multi-stage rocket engine?

31 The Space Shuttle

Reusable parts

Supply list – The space shuttle

☐ Copy of "Space Shuttle" worksheet

What did we learn?

1. What was the main advantage of the space shuttle vehicle over all previous manned space vehicles?

2. What were the main purposes of the shuttle program?

3. What were the two main parts of the orbiter and what were their purposes?

Taking it further

1. Why was the space shuttle called an orbiter?

2. Why was the orbiter shaped like an airplane?

3. Why did the orbiter have to be carried back to Florida if it landed in California?

Name _____   Date_____

🧪 Space Shuttle Worksheet

Use these terms to label the drawing below.

Nose cone   Payload bay

Fuselage   Wing

Rudder   Crew compartment

Tail   Speed brake

Landing gear

1. _____

2. _____

3. _____

4. _____

5. _____

6. _____

7. _____

8. _____

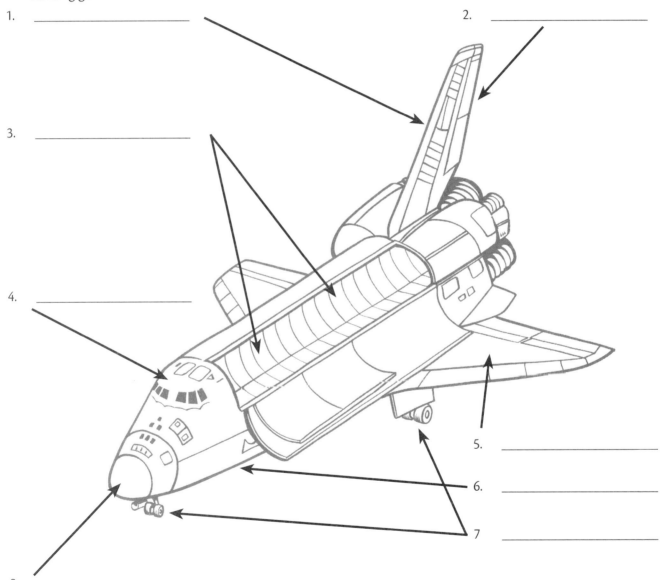

32 International Space Station

Reaching for freedom

 Supply list – Water balls

☐ Water

☐ Waxed paper

☐ Toothpick or knife

What did we learn?

1. What is the International Space Station?

2. Why do countries feel there is a need for a space station?

🚀 Taking it further

1. What shape would you expect a flame to be on the space station?

33 Astronauts

Modern-day explorers

Supply list – Space suits

☐ Winter clothing including hat, gloves, coat, snow pants, and boots

☐ Hand mirror

☐ Building blocks

☐ Nut and bolt

☐ Bicycle helmet or motorcycle helmet with face mask (optional)

Supplies for Challenge – Research an astronaut

☐ Research materials on astronauts

What did we learn?

1. What are some ways that astronauts train for their missions?

2. What conditions in space require astronauts to need spacesuits?

🚀 Taking it further

1. What are some things you can do if you want to become an astronaut?

2. What would you like to do if you were involved in the space program?

34 Solar System Model: Final Project

Showing what's out there

Final Project supply list – Solar system model

Styrofoam™ balls in the following sizes:

☐ 5 in. (1 each)

☐ 4 in. (1 each)

☐ 3 in. (1 each)

☐ 2½ in. (1 each)

☐ 2 in. (1 each)

☐ 1½ in. (2 each)

☐ 1¼ in. (2 each)

☐ Stiff craft wire

☐ 2 Styrofoam™ 4½-inch rings

☐ Paint

Supplies for Challenge – Planet statistics

☐ Index cards

What did we learn?

1. What holds all of the planets in orbit around the sun?

2.   What other items are in our solar system that are not included in your model?

**Taking it further**

1.   Why do the planets orbit the sun and not the earth?

35 Conclusion

Reflecting on our universe

 Supply list – Reflecting on God's wonderful creation

☐ Bible

☐ Flashlight

☐ Blanket

☐ Night sky

What did we learn?

1. What is the best thing you learned about our universe?

Earth Science Worksheets

for Use with

Our Planet Earth

(***God's Design: Heaven & Earth***)

1 Introduction to Earth Science

The study of our world

 Supply list – The earth is reliable

☐ Tennis ball

☐ String

☐ Masking tape

 What did we learn?

1. What are the four main studies of earth science?

2. What is one question mentioned in this lesson that science cannot answer about the earth?

3. Why can we rely on God's Word to tell us where the earth came from?

🚀 Taking it further

1. How does the first law of thermodynamics confirm the Genesis account of creation?

2. How does the second law of thermodynamics confirm the Genesis account of creation?

3. Read Psalm 139:8–10. What do these verses say about where we can find God?

2 Introduction to Geology

The study of the earth itself

🧪 Supply list – Geology scavenger hunt

☐ Copy of "Geology Scavenger Hunt" worksheet

🎖 Supplies for Challenge – Elements

☐ "Periodic Table of the Elements" (in student manual)

☐ Packaged food with nutrition labels

🧠 What did we learn?

1. What is geology?

2. What are some of the evidences that God designed the earth uniquely to support life?

🚀 Taking it further

1. List some ways that geology affects your life on a regular basis.

2. What area of geology interests you the most?

🧪 Geology Scavenger Hunt Worksheet

Identify the following items made from common minerals and metals by their not-so-common descriptions.

1. Gallon of hydrogen, oxygen, and calcium _____

2. Tube of fluoride _____

3. Box of sodium chloride _____

4. Box of O-shaped phosphorous, iron, zinc, copper, and calcium _____

5. Wooden tubes filled with graphite _____

6. Sticks of limestone or gypsum _____

7. Box of phosphorus and sulfur-tipped sticks _____

8. Talc used on babies _____

9. Nickel-cadmium rechargeable units _____

10. Gypsum board used for home construction _____

11. Silicon squares _____

12. Disks of copper-covered zinc _____

13. Electricity-conducting copper lines _____

14. Mercury-filled medical instrument _____

15. U-shaped iron for holding papers together _____

3 The Earth's History

How it all began

Supply list – Flood in a jar

☐ Large jar with lid

☐ Rocks, pebbles, sand, dirt

☐ Water

 What did we learn?

1. What are the two most popular views for how the earth became what it is today?

2. According to the Bible, what are the three major events that affected the way the earth looks today?

3. Should a good scientist disregard evidence that contradicts his/her ideas?

4. Have scientists proven that evolution is true?

5. Have scientists proven that biblical creation is true?

🚀 Taking it further

1. How might scientists explain the discovery of fossilized seashells in the middle of a desert?

2. Explain how a fossilized tree could be found upright through several layers of rock.

The Genesis Flood

God's punishment for sin

🧪 Supply list – Picture of the original earth

☐ Paper

☐ Drawing materials (colored pencils, markers, etc.)

🎖 Supplies for Challenge – Did the Flood really happen?

☐ Copy of "Did the Flood Really Happen?" worksheet

🧠 What did we learn?

1. What are some things geologists observe that point to a worldwide flood?

2. What major geological events may have been associated with the Flood of Noah's day?

🚀 Taking it further

1. How would a huge flood change the way the earth looks?

2. Why did God send a huge flood?

Name _____   Date_____

🏅 Did the Flood Really Happen? Worksheet

What would you expect to see if the earth was covered by a raging flood of water? Write YES next to each description that would probably happen in a flood and NO next to each description that would probably not happen.

1. _____ Water would wash away rocks, soil, and buildings.

2. _____ Millions of animals and people would die.

3. _____ The water would move rocks and soil from one place to another.

4 _____ Buildings would be destroyed.

5. _____ Land would be unchanged.

6. _____ A large boat would float on the water.

7. _____ Land animals would be covered with mud and sand.

8. _____ Debris would settle out of the water.

9. _____ Plants would not be uprooted or killed.

10. _____ New paths would be formed for water to flow through.

You should be getting a picture of what the whole world would have looked like after the Flood. You may have seen pictures of areas where hurricanes have hit or floods have come through. The area is often totally devastated by all the wind and water. This is how the earth would have looked after the Flood. Every building would have been destroyed. Every air-breathing, land-dwelling animal and every person that was not on the Ark would have died. Massive amounts of dirt, sand, and other debris would have been moved from one place to another. With this in mind, list at least three things that you would expect to find hundreds or even thousands of years later when you dig into the earth.

1. _____

2. _____

3. _____

5 The Great Ice Age

The age of woolly mammoths

Supply list – Ice Age crossword puzzle

☐ Copy of "Ice Age Crossword Puzzle"

Supplies for Challenge – Ice Age ideas

☐ Copy of "World Map"

☐ World atlas with climate map of world

☐ Crayons or markers

What did we learn?

1. What two conditions are necessary for an ice age?

2. How did the Genesis Flood set up conditions for the Ice Age?

3. How do evolutionists explain the needed conditions for multiple ice ages?

1. Do you think there are new glaciers still forming today?

Name _____   Date_____

🧪 Ice Age Crossword Puzzle

Across

3. A large body of salt water that was warmer during the Ice Age than today.

6. Extinct hairy elephant that lived during the Ice Age.

7. A continuous ice cover extending between landmasses over which animals and/or people may have migrated.

10. A thick sheet of ice that does not completely melt.

11. The covering of the earth with water that occurred during the time of Noah.

12. The planet that was covered by a worldwide Flood.

Down

1. What happened to large quantities of water during the Ice Age as it passed from liquid to a solid by loss of heat.

2. The time when much of the earth was covered with snow and glaciers.

4. Tiny fragments of solid rock that come out of a volcano that can block sunlight.

5. The weather conditions in a location averaged over a long period of time.

8. How the temperature felt in Canada during the Ice Age.

9. What is believed to have put ash into the air after the Flood contributing to summers being cooler than today.

13. A boat built by Noah to save his family and animals from the Flood.

Name _____

Date _____

◉ World Map

Images © Map Resources

6 Glaciers

Ice that never melts

⚗️ Supply list – How glaciers form

☐ Tall narrow jar such as an olive jar

☐ Marshmallows

☐ Cardboard

☐ Small heavy weights

🧠 What did we learn?

1. What is a glacier?

2. How does a glacier form?

3. What are the three types of glaciers?

4. What is calving?

🚀 Taking it further

1. Why do glaciers exist mostly at the poles and on high mountain tops?

2. Why is it cold enough to prevent glaciers from melting at the North Pole, when there is 20–24 hours of sunlight during the summer?

7 Movement of Glaciers

Slowly creeping down the valley

🧪 Supply list – Making a mini-glacier

☐ Water, sand, and pebbles

☐ Gloves

☐ Empty half-gallon milk carton

Note: This activity requires the water to freeze overnight. You may want to start it the day before you do the lesson.

🏅 Supplies for Challenge – The force of water

☐ Glass jar with lid

☐ Newspaper

☐ Plastic zipper bag

☐ Work gloves

☐ Freezer

🧠 What did we learn?

1. What is the shape of a valley carved by glaciers?

2. How do glaciers pick up rocks and other debris?

3. What is the name of the line of rocks that marks the farthest advance of the glacier?

🚀 Taking it further

1. How might a scientist tell how far a glacier moved a rock or boulder?

2. Why do glaciers often have deep cracks and crevices?

⚗️ Making a mini-glacier

1. How did the movement of the ice affect the surface of the hill?

2. Can you see striations — lines made in the dirt by the sand and pebbles in the ice?

3. Is there a line of dirt and rocks at the front edge of the glacier?

4. What did you see after the ice melted? Is there an area of pebbles that moved with the glacier?

Design of the Earth

Blueprint for the planet

🧪 Supply list

Making a model of earth

☐ 1 gumball per child

☐ Bowl

☐ Chocolate chips

☐ Wax paper

☐ 1 toothpick per child

☐ 1 large marshmallow per child

Seismic waves

☐ Serving bowl

☐ Small bottle or jar

☐ Pencil

🏅 Supplies for Challenge – Earth's composition

☐ Chocolate chips

☐ Plastic zipper bag

☐ Cup

☐ Water

☐ Paper

☐ Protractor

☐ Pencil

☐ Bowl

🧠 What did we learn?

1. What do most scientists believe to be the three main parts of the earth?

2. Which is the thickest part of the earth?

3. Which is the thinnest part of the earth?

4. Where is the crust the thickest?

Taking it further

1. Why do scientists believe the mantle is hotter and denser than the crust?

2. For what other things, besides the interior of the earth, do scientists have to develop models without actually seeing what they are describing?

9 Rocks

Boulders, rocks, gravel, pebbles . . .

🧪 Supply list – Rock cycle

☐ Copy of "The Rock Cycle" worksheet

🎖 Supplies for Challenge – Identifying rocks

☐ Several rocks

🧠 What did we learn?

1. What are rocks made from?

2. What are the three categories of rocks?

3. How is igneous rock formed?

4. How is sedimentary rock formed?

5. How is metamorphic rock formed?

🚀 Taking it further

1. Why are rocks important?

2. Where is a good place to look for rocks?

3. Why is it better to store your rock samples in a box with dividers than in a bag?

⚗ The Rock Cycle Worksheet

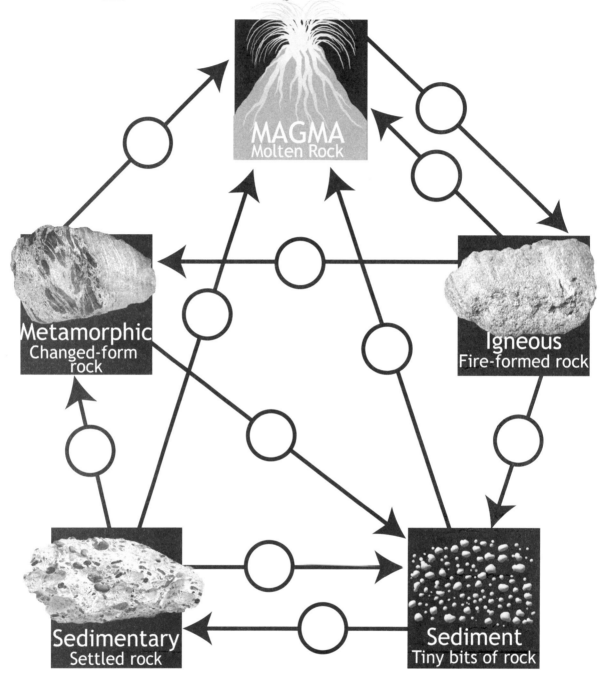

Place the correct process number from the list below in each box to describe how that rock or item is formed. (Note: Most processes are used more than once.)

1. Cooling into a solid

2. Weathering and breaking apart

3. Settling, pressing, and cementing together

4. Heat, pressure, and time

5. Melting only

10 Igneous Rocks

Fire rocks

🧪 Supply list – Growing crystals

☐ Alum

☐ Saucepan

☐ Water

☐ 2 craft sticks

☐ 2 paper or plastic cups

☐ Stove

☐ Refrigerator

🏅 Supplies for Challenge – Identifying igneous rock

☐ Several samples of igneous rocks

☐ Rocks and minerals guide

☐ Magnifying glass

☐ Raw sugar

☐ Brown sugar

☐ Butterscotch candy

🧠 What did we learn?

1. What is the difference between magma and lava?

2. How are extrusive rocks formed?

3. How are intrusive rocks formed?

🚀 Taking it further

1. Which kind of igneous rocks have the largest crystals?

2. Why is granite commonly used in buildings and monuments?

3. Do all rocks sink in water?

4. Why not?

5. Where are you likely to find pumice?

11 Sedimentary Rocks

Layers of sediment

 Supply list – Making sedimentary rock / a sedimentary lunch

- ☐ 2 cups of sand
- ☐ 1 cup of cornstarch
- ☐ Old saucepan
- ☐ Paint (optional)
- ☐ Water
- ☐ Stove
- ☐ Ingredients to make a peanut butter and jelly or lunchmeat sandwich (optional)

Supplies for Challenge – Lithification

- ☐ 2 paper cups
- ☐ Plaster of Paris
- ☐ Smooth pebbles
- ☐ Spoon
- ☐ Rocks and minerals guide
- ☐ Rough pebbles (like aquarium rocks)

What did we learn?

1. How are sedimentary rocks formed?

2. Were all sedimentary rocks formed during the Flood?

🚀 Taking it further

1. Why are fossils found in sedimentary rocks?

2. Sediment is simply any small piece of something that settles out of a liquid. What sediment might you find around your house or in nature?

12 Fossils

How do we know what dinosaurs looked like?

🧪 Supply list – Making your own fossils

☐ Plaster of Paris

☐ Modeling clay

☐ Petroleum jelly

☐ Cup and spoon

☐ Shell or other item to "fossilize"

🧠 What did we learn?

1. How does an animal become a fossil?

2. What are the two different types of fossils?

3. What types of creatures are most fossils?

🚀 Taking it further

1. How many true transitional fossils, ones showing one creature evolving into another kind, have been found?

2. What does this indicate about the idea that land animals evolved from sea creatures?

3. What are some things we can learn from fossils?

4. What kinds of things cannot be learned from fossils?

13 Fossil Fuels

A major energy source

🧪 Supply list – Fossilized bones

☐ 2 sponges

☐ Epsom salt

☐ Shallow dish or pan

☐ Scissors

☐ Food coloring (optional)

🎗 Supplies for Challenge – Geologic column

☐ Copy of "What Would You Expect?" worksheet

🧠 What did we learn?

1. What is the definition of a fossil fuel?

2. What three forms of fossil fuels do we commonly use?

🚀 Taking it further

1. What evidence supports rapid and recent coal formation instead of slow formation millions of years ago?

2. Why is finding natural gas when drilling into the ground a good indicator that oil is nearby?

3. Why is the existence of natural gas an indication that oil was formed only a few thousand years ago?

🏅 What Would You Expect? Worksheet

Suppose there is a volcano in the Rocky Mountains of the western United States. This volcano has been dormant for a very long time and it looks very much like the rest of the mountains around it. There is a lake near the base of the volcano. Imagine that the volcano suddenly erupts. A large area around the volcano is covered with mud and ash.

If you went back to the area a hundred years later and dug through the layers of hardened ash and mud, what would you expect to find? Place each of the following items in the layer you would expect to find it.

Pine needles	Deer	Sea shells	Snakes
Flies	Scrub oak	Wild flowers	Parrots
Palm trees	Algae	Ground squirrels	Rabbits
Fish	Coconuts	Crawdads	Crows

Lowest level	Upper level	Not found

1. Briefly explain why you put the items where you did.

_____

_____

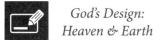

14 Metamorphic Rocks

Let's make a change

Supply list – Morphing ice / Making marble

☐ Copy of "Morphing Ice" worksheet

☐ Wax paper

☐ Washcloth

☐ Bowl

☐ Shallow dish

☐ Saucepan

☐ Shaved ice (or snow if available)

☐ 2 or 3 pieces of different colored taffy or other soft candy

☐ Stove

Supplies for Challenge – Types of metamorphic rocks

☐ Copy of "Metamorphic Match" worksheet

☐ Rocks and minerals guide

What did we learn?

1. What are the three ingredients needed to change igneous or sedimentary rock into metamorphic rock?

2. Why is marble often swirled instead of pure white?

🚀 Taking it further

1. Why is metamorphic rock often used for sculptures and monuments?

2. Why is metamorphic rock hard and durable?

Name _____   Date_____

🧪 Morphing Ice Worksheet

The three "ingredients," or conditions, needed to change igneous or sedimentary rock into metamorphic rock are heat, pressure, and time. To better understand how these three conditions affect rocks, perform the following experiments with shaved ice, or with snow if you have it available.

Heat only

Place one-quarter of the shaved ice in a saucepan and heat it over medium heat for 1 minute. What happened to the snow?

_____

What do you suppose happens to igneous or sedimentary rock that is heated but does not experience pressure?

_____

Pressure only

Place one-quarter of the shaved ice in a shallow dish. Quickly slap the ice with your hand. What happened to the ice?

_____

What do you suppose happens to igneous or sedimentary rock that experiences a quick burst of pressure such as being hit with something?

_____

Time only

Place one-quarter of the shaved ice in a bowl and place the bowl in the freezer for five minutes. What happened to the ice?

_____

What do you suppose happens to igneous or sedimentary rock that stays at about the same temperature for a long time without additional pressure?

_____

Heat, pressure, and time

Take the remaining shaved ice and squeeze it into a ball. Squeeze for a full minute (wrap ice in a washcloth if it is too cold to handle). Now examine the ball of ice. How does it compare to the shaved ice or snow?

_____

What do you suppose happens to igneous or sedimentary rock that experiences heat and pressure over time?

_____

🎖 Metamorphic Match Worksheet

Use a rocks and minerals guide book to help you match the following igneous and sedimentary rocks to the metamorphic rock each becomes.

Igneous/Sedimentary   **Metamorphic**

_____ Granite   A. Slate

_____ Shale   B. Schist

_____ Sandstone   C. Gneiss

_____ Limestone   D. Quartzite

_____ Mica   E. Amphibolite

_____ Basalt   F. Hornblende

_____ Dolerite   G. Marble

15 Minerals

Animal, vegetable, or mineral?

🧪 Supply list – Mineral scavenger hunt

☐ Copy of "Mineral Scavenger Hunt" worksheet

🎖 Supplies for Challenge – Mancala

☐ Egg carton

☐ 48 small rocks or pebbles

☐ A coin

🧠 What did we learn?

1. What five requirements must a substance meet in order to be classified as a mineral?

2. What is a native mineral?

3. What is a compound?

🚀 Taking it further

1. Are there any minerals that are mixtures?

2. What is the difference between a rock and a mineral?

3. Is coal a mineral?

4. Are all minerals considered rocks?

5. Are all rocks considered minerals?

6. Where are you likely to find minerals?

⚗️ Mineral Scavenger Hunt Worksheet

Before you can go looking for minerals, you need to understand what a mineral is and what it is not. Explain why each of the following items is not a mineral.

1. Water _____

2. Steel _____

3. Coal _____

4. Cookies _____

5. Glass _____

Now that you know why some items are not considered minerals, let's see if you can find some items that are considered minerals. Take a minute to review the five requirements for a mineral, then search throughout your house for minerals. Some places to look might include the kitchen (read food labels), the bathroom (look at vitamin bottle labels and toothpaste), your piggy bank, and your garage. List some of the minerals you found on the lines below.

Minerals around my house include:

_____

_____

_____

_____

_____

_____

_____

_____

_____

16 Identifying Minerals

Is it salt or sugar?

🧪 Supply list – Mineral identification

☐ Magnifying glass

☐ Eye protection (goggles)

☐ Masking tape

☐ Penny

☐ Hammer

☐ Old drinking glass

☐ Old pillowcase or towel

☐ Unglazed ceramic tile

☐ Rocks and minerals guide

☐ Copy of "Mineral Identification" worksheet

☐ Samples of 3 or 4 minerals (quartz, feldspar, mica, limestone, etc.)

🏅 Supplies for Challenge – Rocks and minerals

☐ Copy of "Is It a Rock or a Mineral?" worksheet

☐ Rocks and minerals guide

🧠 What did we learn?

1. What are some common tests used to identify minerals?

2. Why is color alone not a sufficient test?

🚀 Taking it further

1. Is crystal size a good test for identifying a mineral? Why or why not?

2. What is the difference between cleavage and fracture?

3. Why do some tests need to be done in a laboratory?

4. How can you tell a sample of sugar from a sample of salt?

Name _____   Date_____

⚗️ Mineral Identification Worksheet

Sample #				
Color				
Streak				
Luster				
Crystal shape				
Hardness				
Cleavage				
Identity				

🏅 Is It a Rock or a Mineral? Worksheet

Answer the questions for each item listed below.

Item	Is it an element, compound, or mixture?	What are its main components?	Is it a rock or a mineral?
Gold			
Granite			
Feldspar			
Quartz			
Limestone			
Copper			
Diamond			
Obsidian			
Gypsum			
Shale			

17 Valuable Minerals

How much for an ounce of gold?

🧪 Supply list – Chocolate mining

☐ Chocolate chip cookie

☐ Toothpicks

🧠 What did we learn?

1. What are some valuable minerals?

2. What is a native mineral?

3. What are some important uses for gold?

4. What are some important uses for silver?

🚀 Taking it further

1. Why is diamond considered an exception among minerals?

2. Diamonds and coal are both made from carbon. What makes them different?

Natural & Artificial Gems

Cut stones

 Supply list – Breastplate worksheet

☐ Copy of "Breastplate" worksheet

☐ Colored pencils, markers, or crayons

Supplies for Challenge – Beautiful gems

☐ Pictures of various gems

☐ Visit a mineral exhibit at a museum (optional)

What did we learn?

1. What is a gem?

2. How is a gem different from a native mineral?

3. How are artificial rubies made?

Taking it further

1. What can you guess about the temperatures at which synthetic rubies are formed?

2. Why would rubies be formed at high temperatures?

3. What are some disadvantages of synthetic gems?

4. Why are natural gems worth more money than artificial gems?

🧪 Breastplate Worksheet

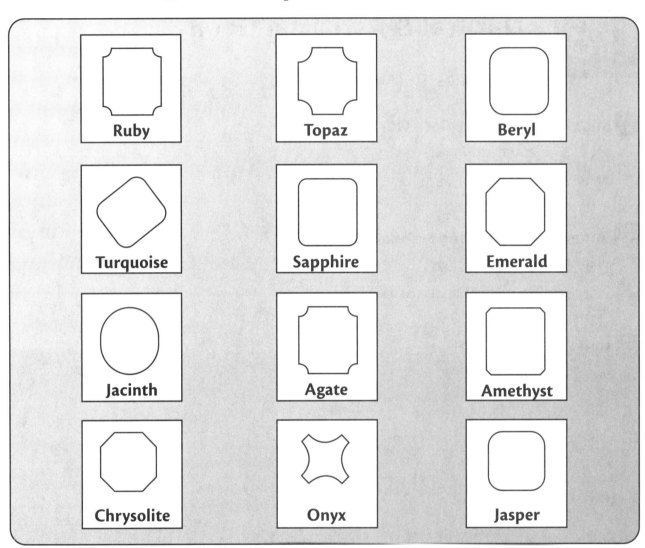

Ruby—Dark red

Topaz—Yellow to brown

Beryl—Green, bluish green, yellow, pink, or white

Turquoise—Light greenish blue

Sapphire—Deep blue

Emerald—Bright or deep green

Jacinth—Orange

Agate—Striped or marbled in any color

Amethyst—Deep purple

Chrysolite—Green

Onyx—Translucent to black

Jasper—Blackish green

19 Plate Tectonics

Slip sliding away

Supply list – Rodinia puzzle

☐ Copy of "World Map" (Lesson 5)

☐ Scissors

☐ Tracing paper

☐ Tape

Supplies for Challenge – Plate movements

☐ Graham crackers

☐ Wax paper

☐ Creamy peanut butter or frosting

What did we learn?

1. What is plate tectonics?

2. How many plates do scientists think there are?

🚀 Taking it further

1. What are some things that are believed to have happened in the past because of the movement of the tectonic plates?

2. What are some things that happen today because of the movement of the tectonic plates?

20 Mountains

Don't make a mountain out of a mole hill

🧪 Supply list – Famous mountains

☐ Copy of "Famous Mountains" worksheet

☐ Bible

🎖 Supplies for Challenge – Mountain ranges

☐ Copy of "World Map"

☐ Atlas or topographical map of the world

🧠 What did we learn?

1. What is a mountain?

2. What is a mountain range?

3. What is the difference between actual height and elevation of a mountain?

🚀 Taking it further

1. Where are the mountains with the highest elevations located?

2. Is a 700-foot rise a mountain or a hill?

⚗ Famous Mountains Worksheet

The Bible makes references to mountains over 300 times. Some of the mountain names should be very familiar to you. Use a Bible to help you match the mountain to the important event or events that took place there.

1. _____ Mountains of Ararat

2. _____ Mount Sinai

3. _____ Mount Moriah

4. _____ Mount Carmel

5. _____ Mount of Olives

6. _____ Mount of Transfiguration

7. _____ Mount Horeb (The Mountain of God)

A. Peter, James, and John saw Jesus transformed (Matthew 17:1–2)

B. Moses saw a burning bush; Elijah hid from Jezebel (Exodus 3:1–3; 1 Kings 19:1–8)

C. Noah's Ark landed here (Genesis 8:4)

D. Elijah defeated the prophets of Baal (1 Kings 18:18–40)

E. Moses received the Law from God (Exodus 19:1–10)

F. Jesus went to pray, was arrested, and will return here (Luke 22:39–53)

G. Abraham was willing to offer Isaac as a sacrifice (Genesis 22:1–2)

@ World Map

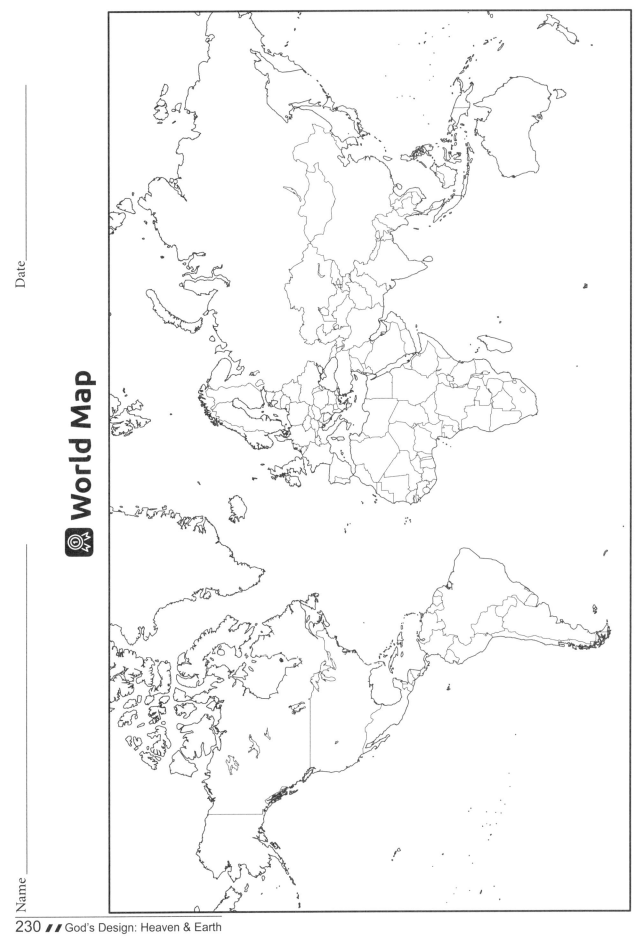

21 Types of Mountains

How did they form?

Supply list – Paper fold mountains

☐ Newspaper or paper towels

Supplies for Challenge – Fold types

☐ Four or more colors of modeling clay

☐ Knife

What did we learn?

1. How are depositional mountains formed?

2. How are erosional mountains formed?

3. How are fold and fault mountains formed?

🚀 Taking it further

Identify each mountain as either depositional, erosional, or fold. (Outside research is necessary for this question.)

1. Mount St. Helens:

2. Bryce Canyon:

3. Sand Dunes National Monument:

4. Rocky Mountains:

5. Grand Canyon:

6. Mount Everest:

22 Earthquakes

Shake, rattle, and roll

Supply list – Earthquake-proof buildings
☐ 10–20 building blocks

Supplies for Challenge – Faults
☐ Three colors of modeling clay

☐ Knife

What did we learn?

1. What is believed to be the cause of earthquakes?

2. What is an aftershock?

3. What name is given to the area on the earth's surface above where an earthquake originates?

4. What is a fault?

🚀 Taking it further

1. How does the type of material affect the speed of the earthquake waves?

2. How does this change in speed help scientists "see" under the earth's crust?

3. Why are earthquakes in the middle of the ocean so dangerous?

⚗️ Earthquake-proof buildings

4. What might architects do to help make buildings stronger?

5. What shape of building is more likely to withstand an earthquake?

Detecting & Predicting Earthquakes

Predicting the "Big One"

Supply list – Making a seismograph

☐ Shoebox

☐ Rolling pin

☐ Paper

☐ Pencil

☐ Tape

Supplies for Challenge – Earthquake locations

☐ Copy of "World Map" from Lesson 20

☐ Access to the Internet

What did we learn?

1. What is the difference between the magnitude and the intensity of an earthquake?

2. What are three factors that determine how much damage is done by an earthquake?

3. Explain how a seismograph works.

4. What people group was first to record earthquake measurements?

🚀 Taking it further

1. What are some ways people have learned to prepare for earthquakes?

2. What should you do if you are in an earthquake?

24 Volcanoes

Fire mountains

⚗ Supply list – Volcano model

☐ Baking soda

☐ Vinegar

☐ Empty bottle

☐ Newspaper

☐ Tape

☐ Baking sheet

☐ Red food coloring (optional)

🏅 Supplies for Challenge – Volcano locations

☐ World map from previous lessons

☐ World atlas

🧠 What did we learn?

1. What are the three stages or states of a volcano?

2. Describe the three main parts of a volcano.

3. Give the name for each of the following items that are emitted from a volcano:

    a. Liquid or melted rock:

    b. Tiny bits of solid rock:

    c. Pieces of rock from 0.2 to 1 inch (0.5–2.5 cm) in diameter:

    d. Blobs of lava that solidify in the air:

    e. Steam and carbon dioxide:

🚀 Taking it further

1. How might a volcano become active without anyone noticing?

2. How are volcanoes and earthquakes related?

3. How certain can we be that a volcano is really extinct?

25   Volcano Types

Is there more than one?

🧪 Supply list – Cool volcano

☐ Pie pan

☐ Cookie crumbs

☐ ½ gallon of ice cream

☐ Chocolate chips

☐ Chocolate syrup

🎖 Supplies for Challenge – Volcanoes of the past

☐ Unopened can of soft drink

🧠 What did we learn?

1. What are the three shapes of volcanoes, and how is each formed?

2. Where are most active volcanoes located today?

3. What are some of the dangers of volcanoes?

4. What are some positive side effects of volcanoes?

🚀 Taking it further

1. How do black sand beaches form?

26 Mount St. Helens

God's gift to scientists

Supply list – Volcano word search

☐ Copy of "Volcano Word Search"

What did we learn?

1. Describe some of the ways the data collected at Mount St. Helens is challenging evolutionary thinking.

Taking it further

1. How did the ash from the eruption of Mount St. Helens affect the weather in 1980?

2. How could volcanic activity have contributed to the onset of the Ice Age?

🧪 Volcano Word Search

Find the following words in the puzzle below. Words may be horizontal, vertical, or diagonal, including backward.

Lava	Subduction	Caldera	Extinct
Cinder	Composite	Active	Bomb
Magma	Shield	Crater	Pahoehoe
Eruption	Cone	Dormant	

```
A  D  O  P  X  Y  B  A  E  P  A  H  D  S  H
C  O  D  O  R  M  A  N  T  E  R  A  C  T  C
E  X  S  N  M  K  L  A  I  O  T  C  A  E  R
P  A  H  O  E  H  O  E  A  S  M  A  G  R  O
U  U  R  S  I  N  D  R  C  H  A  P  T  U  O
C  U  S  U  B  D  U  C  T  I  O  N  P  P  Q
O  A  U  L  I  N  S  I  I  E  E  C  R  T  E
M  A  G  M  A  O  M  N  V  L  X  Y  Z  I  O
P  L  M  K  R  V  Z  D  E  D  T  U  X  O  P
O  S  W  Q  B  O  A  E  L  I  I  F  F  N  A
S  C  L  R  E  T  A  R  C  A  N  P  O  S  T
I  T  S  U  I  O  B  O  M  B  C  S  H  I  L
T  C  N  E  D  R  N  H  F  R  T  W  K  L  J
E  C  A  L  D  E  R  A  E  T  X  N  T  M  I
R  W  I  O  P  R  Q  C  M  I  O  R  S  L  P
```

27 Geysers

Heated ground water

 Supply list – Make a geyser

☐ Flexible soda straw

☐ Cup filled with water

What did we learn?

1. What are some ways that heated ground water shows up on the surface of the earth?

2. Explain how a geyser works.

3. How is a mud pot different from a hot spring?

Taking it further

1. How might a scientist figure out which irregular geysers are connected underground?

2. Why do some hot pools have a rainbow appearance?

3. Can you tell the temperature of the water just by looking at a pool?

Challenge questions – Geothermal energy

1. Why are geothermal power plants mostly located near edges of tectonic plates?

2. Would you expect geothermal power plants to experience more or fewer earthquakes than other power plants?

3. Why is geothermal energy considered a renewable resource?

28 Weathering & Erosion

It's wearing me down

🧪 Supply list – Weathering at work

☐ Copy of "Weathering" worksheet

☐ Vinegar

☐ Bar of soap

☐ Soda straw

☐ Modeling clay

☐ Real chalk (made from limestone) or a limestone rock

☐ Sink

🎖️ Supplies for Challenge – Chemical weathering

☐ Copy of "Chemical Erosion" worksheet

☐ Steel wool (without soap)

☐ 3 plastic zipper bags

☐ Gloves

🧠 What did we learn?

1. What is weathering?

2. Describe the two types of weathering.

🚀 Taking it further

1. How does freezing and thawing of water break rocks?

2. In what ways do people use water or other materials to remove the surface of something in a process similar to mechanical weathering?

🧪 Weathering Worksheet

Chemical Weathering

Slowly drop a few drops of vinegar on a piece of limestone chalk or a limestone rock.

1. What did you observe as the vinegar came in contact with the limestone? _____

    _____

2. How did the limestone look afterward? _____

The vinegar reacted with the limestone to produce carbon dioxide and wear away some of the material. Carbon dioxide mixes with water to form an acid that reacts the same way with many rocks — wearing them away.

Mechanical Weathering 1

Set a bar of soap in a sink and allow the water from the faucet to slowly drip on it. Allow the dripping to continue for several hours.

3. How did the dripping of the water affect the surface of the soap? _____

    _____

Dripping of water can affect rocks the same way. It just takes more time or more water.

Mechanical Weathering 2

Plug one end of a soda straw with modeling clay. Fill the straw completely with water. Plug the other end of the straw with clay. Place the straw in the freezer for several hours.

4. How did the clay and straw change when the water froze? _____

    _____

5. What effects might freezing water have on rocks? _____

🎖 Chemical Erosion Worksheet

Steel wool is made of mostly iron, so you will be testing the effects of oxidation on iron. Always use gloves when handling steel wool.

1. How does the steel wool feel? How strong or stiff is it? _____

_____

Form three golf-ball-sized balls of steel wool. Label three plastic zipper bags A, B, and C. Place one ball of steel wool into bag A. Push out as much air as possible and seal the bag. Moisten one of the remaining balls of steel wool with water and place it in bag B. Again, push out as much air as possible and seal the bag. Moisten the last ball of steel wool and place it in bag C. Gently blow into the bag to fill it with air and seal the bag with as much air inside as possible.

2. In which bag do you expect to see the most rust after 5 days? _____

Observe the steel wool inside each bag daily for 5 days. Record your observations below.

Day	Bag A	Bag B	Bag C
1			
2			
3			
4			
5			

Using gloves, remove the steel wool from each bag and feel each piece. Record your observations below.

Bag A	Bag B	Bag C

3. Which bag had the wool with the most rust? _____

4. Did this agree with your initial guess? _____

5. Why do you think this sample had the most rust? _____

_____

29 Mass Wasting

The force of gravity

 Supply list – Observing mass wasting

☐ Baking tray or large baking pan

☐ Soil and rocks

☐ Water

What did we learn?

1. What is mass wasting?

2. What is slow movement of the soil and rocks down a slope called?

3. What is rapid or sudden movement of the soil and rocks called?

🚀 Taking it further

1. How does water affect mass wasting?

2. How might weathermen predict when the avalanche danger is high?

30 Stream Erosion

The power of moving water

Supply list – Terracing

☐ 3 baking dishes

☐ Soil

☐ Leaves, grass, or other plant material

☐ Book at least 2 inches thick

☐ Cup of water

Supplies for Challenge – Stream erosion

☐ Soil

☐ 3 paper cups

☐ Pencil

☐ Access to an oven

☐ Water

What did we learn?

1. What is the most powerful eroding force?

2. How does gravity cause stream erosion?

3. What is the gradient of a river?

🚀 Taking it further

1. Why are farmers concerned about soil erosion?

2. What are some steps farmers take to prevent water from eroding their topsoil?

3. Besides water, what other natural force can erode topsoil?

4. What can farmers do to protect their topsoil from wind erosion?

5. Why do lakes and reservoirs have to be dredged, emptied, and dug out periodically?

31   Soil

Isn't it just dirt?

🧪 Supply list – Examining soil

☐ Potting soil

☐ Soil from your yard

☐ Magnifying glass

🎖 Supplies for Challenge – Soil study

☐ Copy of "Permeability of Soil" worksheet

☐ 4 paper cups

☐ 2–3 cups of soil from your yard

☐ Newspaper

☐ Colander

☐ Fine-mesh strainer

☐ Stopwatch

☐ Liquid measuring cup

☐ Pencils

☐ Baking sheet

🧠 What did we learn?

1. What are the major components of soil?

2. What is the most important element in soil for encouraging plant growth?

🚀 Taking it further

1. What type of rocks would you expect to find near an area with sandy soil?

2. What type of rocks would you expect to find near an area with clay soil?

3. How does a river that regularly floods, such as the Nile, restore lost topsoil?

4. What are some ways that farmers restore nutrients to the soil?

Name _____   Date_____

🏅 Permeability of Soil Worksheet

You will be testing the permeability of four different soil samples. Record your observations below.

Sample	Describe the texture and size of soil in this sample.	Water flow time (seconds)	Water flow amount (ounces)	Permeability (ounces/sec.)
1				
2				
3				
4				

1. Which sample had the highest permeability? _____

2. Which had the lowest permeability? _____

3. How did your unsifted sample (sample 1) compare to the sifted samples? _____

   _____

4. How does particle size affect permeability? _____

   _____

32 Grand Canyon

Lots of time, little water or lots of water, little time?

🧪 Supply list – Grand Canyon model

☐ Modeling clay

☐ Paper

☐ Markers

🧠 What did we learn?

1. What is the main controversy between evolutionists and creationists concerning the formation of Grand Canyon?

2. What evidence shows radiometric dating methods to be unreliable?

⚙ Taking it further

1. What event at the eruption of Mount St. Helens supports the biblical view of how Grand Canyon was formed? (Hint: Review Lesson 30.)

2. How can scientists look at similar data and draw different conclusions?

3. How can we know what to believe when scientists disagree?

33 Caves

Underground wonderlands

🧪 Supply list – Growing stalagmites & stalactites

☐ 2 paper or plastic cups

☐ Cotton string

☐ Epsom salt

☐ Cardboard

☐ Hot water

☐ Scissors

🎗 Supplies for Challenge – Cave research

☐ Research materials on caves

🧠 What did we learn?

1. How are the beautiful formations in caves formed?

2. What is a stalactite?

3. What is a stalagmite?

🚀 Taking it further

1. What evidence do we have that formations in caves can develop rapidly?

2. Why is it likely that calcite formations would have formed rapidly after the Flood?

3. Besides in caves, where can calcite deposits be found?

34 Rocks & Minerals Collection: Final Project

Putting it all together

🧪 Final Project supply list – Rocks & minerals collection

☐ Rocks and minerals guide

☐ Samples of rocks, gems, and minerals

☐ Glue

☐ Markers

☐ Tagboard or poster board

☐ Display box with separated sections (optional)

🧠 What did we learn?

1. What are the three types of rocks?

2. What is a native mineral?

🚀 Taking it further

1. What are some of the greatest or most interesting things you learned from your study of our planet earth?

2. Read Genesis chapters 1 and 2. Discuss what was created on each day and how each part completes the whole.

3. What earth science topic would you like to learn more about?

35 Conclusion

The wonder of our planet earth

 **Supply list – Recognizing God's hand in designing our planet**

☐ Bible

☐ Paper and pencil

Weather & Water Quizzes and Final Exam

for Use with

Our Weather & Water

(*God's Design: Heaven & Earth*)

Atmosphere & Meteorology

Short answer (5 points each answer):

1. What does it mean to have a Christian view of weather? _____

2. Name **three** things you might find in a local weather report. _____

_____   _____

3. What is the outermost part of the atmosphere called? _____

4. What **three** events recorded in the Bible drastically affected the surface of the earth? _____

_____   _____

5. List **three** ways the atmosphere protects life on earth. _____

_____   _____

6. What are scientists called who study the atmosphere? _____

7. What is temperature? _____

8. What causes air pressure? _____

9. What is absolute humidity? _____

10. What is relative humidity? _____

11. What is precipitation? _____

12. What is the major cause of wind? _____

13. Weather occurs in which part of the atmosphere? _____

14. What happens to the atmospheric pressure as you go up in altitude? _____

_____

Challenge questions

Short answer (10 points each answer):

15. Name **two** Christian scientists from the past. _____

_____

16. What is lapse rate with respect to the atmosphere? _____

_____

17. Name **two** gases that are lighter than air. _____

_____

18. Briefly explain how each of the following contributes to weather formation.

Sun: _____

Earth: _____

Air: _____

Water: _____

19. Does temperature always decrease with altitude? Explain your answer. _____

_____

Ancient Weather & Climate

Match the term with its definition (5 points each answer):

1. _____ Conditions in the atmosphere at a given time.

2. _____ Average weather conditions over a long time.

3. _____ Very dry climate.

4. _____ Wet, warm climate year round.

5. _____ How plants were watered in the beginning.

6. _____ Event believed to be triggered by the Flood.

7. _____ Trapping of heat in the earth's atmosphere.

8. _____ Increase in Earth's average temperature due to increased carbon dioxide.

9. _____ Climate with four distinct seasons.

10. _____ Climate with cooler winters than tropical areas.

A. Tropical

B. Ice Age

C. Climate

D. Greenhouse effect

E. Global warming

F. Weather

G. Sub-tropical

H. Stream

I. Desert

j. Temperate

Mark each statement as either True or False (5 points each answer):

11. _____ Average global temperatures have increased in the past 150 years.

12. _____ Carbon dioxide is the main cause of the greenhouse effect.

13. _____ It has been proven that global warming is primarily caused by man's actions.

14. _____ The earth's climate was probably more uniformly tropical before the Flood.

15. _____ The Flood did not change the earth very much.

16. _____ The Bible indicates there may have been one landmass before the Flood.

17. _____ The climate changes from day to day.

18. _____ Deserts can be cold.

19. _____ The monsoon brings rain to much of Southeast Asia.

20. _____ We should just ignore global warming.

Challenge questions

Short answer (20 points each answer):

21. Describe the Coriolis effect. _____

_____

_____

22. In an area that primarily experiences updrafts, would you expect the weather to be wet or dry? Why would you expect this? _____

_____

_____

23. Explain how finding fossils of dinosaurs in Antarctica gives a clue to its past climate. _____

_____

_____

24. How could the climate in an area have changed quickly in the past? _____

_____

_____

25. Give an example of how global warming could be a beneficial thing. _____

_____

_____

Clouds

Fill in the blank with the correct term from below (5 points each answer):

Stratus	Cloud	Six	Cloud seeding
Convection cell	Cumulus	Ten	Transpiration
Evaporation	Nimbus	Snow	Vaporization
Precipitation	Drought	Drizzle	Dew point
Water cycle	Cirrus	Hail	Coalesce

1. Water vapor enters the atmosphere primarily through _____.

2. The _____ describes how water is reused over and over.

3. _____ is water that is leaving the atmosphere.

4. When water vapor condenses in the atmosphere it forms a/an _____.

5. A bubble of warm, moist air is called a/an _____.

6. _____ clouds form in layers or sheets.

7. Big fluffy clouds are called _____ clouds.

8. _____ clouds are wispy and curly.

9. Clouds that are likely to produce rain are called _____ clouds.

10. _____ is large frozen pellets of ice falling from the atmosphere.

11. Water that crystallizes in the clouds and falls to the earth is called _____.

12. As water droplets fall, they begin to _____, meaning they begin to combine with other droplets.

13. _____ are tiny droplets of water too small to be called rain.

14. All snowflakes have _____ sides.

15. _____ is sometimes used to try to produce rain.

16. Only about _____ percent of all clouds produce precipitation.

17. It is called _____ when water vapor is released when a person breathes.

18. _____ occurs when water is heated to the boiling point.

19. The _____ is the point where air holds as much moisture as it can for the current temperature.

20. A long period of time without precipitation is called a/an _____.

Challenge questions

Mark each statement as either True or False (10 points each answer):

17. _____ The water table is the surface of a lake.

18. _____ Water flows through permeable rock.

19. _____ Fog is a cloud that touches the ground.

20. _____ Radiation fog occurs on windy nights.

21. _____ Coastal areas often experience advection fog.

22. _____ Water droplets require a condensation nucleus to coalesce.

23. _____ Upslope fog occurs near mountains.

24. _____ Acid rain is a myth.

25. _____ Rain water is naturally acidic.

26. _____ A spring is formed when ground water finds its way out the side of a hill.

Storms

Choose the best answer for each question or statement (10 points each answer):

1. _____ Most weather is determined by the location and movement of _____.

   A. Meteorologists   B. Air masses   C. Clouds   D. Airplanes

2. _____ When two air masses meet, what do they form?

   A. Weather front   B. Explosion   C. New cloud   D. New mass

3. _____ An air mass has uniform _____.

   A. Humidity   B. Temperature   C. Air pressure   D. A, B, and C

4. _____ Which weather phenomenon keeps temperatures more even on the earth?

   A. Snow   B. Humidity   C. Wind   D. Pressure

5. _____ When the wind blows from the sea to the land it is called a _____.

   A. Sea breeze   B. Land breeze   C. Cool breeze   D. Tsunami

6. _____ Winds that blow straight up consistently are called _____.

   A. Doldrums   B. Prevailing winds   C. Monsoons   D. Seasonal winds

7. _____ About the highest altitude that thunderstorms can reach is _____.

   A. 600 feet   B. 6,000 feet   C. 60,000 feet   D. 600,000 feet

8. _____ God provides a way to return nitrogen to the soil through _____.

   A. Lightning   B. Hail   C. Snow   D. Thunder

9. _____ A spiraling cloud that does not touch the ground is called a _____.

   A. Hurricane   B. Tornado   C. Tsunami   D. Funnel cloud

10. _____ Hurricanes lose power when they _____.

   A. Reach land   B. Suck up water   C. Warm up   D. Stay in one place

Challenge questions

Fill in the blank with the correct term from below (6 points each answer):

East	TOTO	Hurricane	Phased array
West	Mountains	Dropsonde	Doppler
Hurricane hunters	Large lakes	Summer	High altitude winds
Flash flood	Tornadoes	Winter	

11. Scientists measure _____ several times a day to determine where air masses are likely to move.

12. _____ and _____ are two geological features that can affect how weather fronts move.

13. Jet streams are stronger during the _____ than in the _____.

14. Jet streams play a role in the formation of _____.

15. You should climb to higher ground in the event of a/an _____.

16. _____ radar is used to determine the speed and direction that a storm is moving.

17. _____ radar will be able to scan the atmosphere much more quickly than current radar.

18. _____ fly their airplanes through hurricanes and other storms.

19. Weather satellites allow scientists to view all of a/an _____ at one time.

20. _____ was a portable weather station placed in the path of a tornado.

21. A/An _____ is a portable weather station dropped into a hurricane.

22. Because of the jet stream it is often faster to fly from _____ to _____.

Short answer (5 points each answer):

23. Explain the difference between the eye of the hurricane and the eyewall of the hurricane.

24. Explain how a dropsonde helps meteorologists.

Weather Information

Mark each statement as either True or False (5 points each answer):

1. _____ A meteorologist is someone who studies the weather.

2. _____ A barometer is used to measure temperature.

3. _____ Air pressure increases as you go up in altitude.

4. _____ A psychrometer is used to measure relative humidity in the air.

5. _____ All weather sayings are superstitious myths.

6. _____ Meteorologists use many different instruments to understand the weather.

7. _____ Wind direction can be shown by using a wind sock.

8. _____ Weather satellites are very valuable tools for meteorologists.

9. _____ Weather balloons are used to measure the weather on the ground.

10. _____ Doppler radar can help detect severe storms more quickly than regular radar.

11. _____ Computers are very important tools for meteorologists.

12. _____ A weather station model is not useful for conveying information.

13. _____ The National Weather Service helps local meteorologists make forecasts.

14. _____ Weather forecasts were more accurate before computers were used.

15. _____ You can collect weather data at home.

16. _____ An anemometer shows wind direction.

17. _____ With enough information, anyone can predict the weather accurately.

18. _____ Aircrafts and ships are used to help collect weather data.

19. _____ A rain gauge collects rain to show how much precipitation has fallen.

20. _____ God ultimately controls the weather.

Challenge Questions

Match the term with its definition (10 points each answer):

21. _____ Equivalent temperature if the air was dry and still.

22. _____ Calculation using temperature and relative humidity.

23. _____ Calculation using temperature and wind speed.

24. _____ Satellite stays over the same earth location.

25. _____ Satellite moves over the earth's poles.

A. Polar orbit

B. Heat index

C. Apparent temperature

D. Wind chill

E. Geosynchronous orbit

Short answer (25 points each answer):

(Use the charts in Lesson 18 to help determine apparent temperature for each person.)

26. Pete is outside when the temperature is 40°F and the wind is blowing at 15 miles per hour. Polly is outside when the temperature is 30°F and the wind is blowing at 5 miles per hour. Who is likely to feel more comfortable?

27. Paul is outside when the temperature is 90°F and the relative humidity is 50%. Patty is outside when the temperature is 85°F and the relative humidity is 80%. Who is likely to feel more comfortable?

Ocean Movements

Fill in the blank with the correct term (4 points each answer):

1. List the **five** oceans of the world. _____

   _____

2. The _____ winds allowed trade routes to be established in the Indian Ocean.

3. The main mineral dissolved in seawater is _____.

4. There is more oxygen in the ocean near the surface because of _____ growing there.

5. The three main ways that the ocean moves are _____, _____, and
   _____.

6. Cold water is more _____ than warm water, so it sinks.

7. Land near cold water currents tends to have weather that is _____.

8. A body of warm water in the Pacific Ocean that greatly affects weather is _____.

9. The highest point of a wave is called the _____.

10. The lowest point of a wave is called the _____.

Mark each statement as either True or False (4 points each answer):

11. _____ Water molecules are moved hundreds of miles across the ocean by waves.

12. _____ Friction between the air and the water causes waves to form.

13. _____ The highest part of a wave is called the trough.

14. _____ A tsunami is a very dangerous wave.

15. _____ Tides are a result of the gravitational pull of the moon.

16. _____ A rip current can pull a swimmer far out to sea.

17. _____ Erosion from waves is never harmful.

18. _____ Movement of the ocean is beneficial for all life on earth.

19. _____ Weather myths are often based on truth.

Challenge questions

Choose the best answer for each question or statement (10 points each answer):

20. _____ What field of science began with the *Challenger* Expedition in 1872?

    A. Geography   B. Oceanography   C. Astronomy   D. Physics

21. _____How many volumes of information were published after the *Challenger* Expedition?

    A. 50   B. 2   C. 10   D. 1000

22. _____Which is not a method of desalination?

    A. Evaporation   B. Distillation   C. Reverse osmosis   D. Centrifuge

23. _____ Where are the majority of desalination plants located?

    A. Middle East   B. Europe   C. United States   D. Africa

24. _____ Major surface currents combine to form these five major circulations.

    A. Whirlpools   B. Hurricanes   C. Gyres   D. Streams

25. _____ Surface currents and prevailing winds rotate clockwise in the northern hemisphere due to this.

    A. Doppler effect   B. Coriolis effect   C. Phased array   D. Weather effect

26. _____ What scale is used to describe wind and waves in the open ocean?

    A. Fahrenheit   B. Fujita-Pearson   C. Beaufort   D. Saffir-Simpson

27. _____ What is the difference between high tide and low tide called?

    A. Tidal range   B. Tidal barrier   C. Neap tide   D. Spring tide

28. _____ What is a whirlpool caused by changing tides called?

    A. Swirl   B. Hurricane   C. Tornado   D. Maelstrom

29. _____ What erosional land formation closes off the mouth of a bay?

    A. Spur   B. Bay island   C. Bay barrier   D. Spit

Sea Floor

1. **Label the features of the ocean floor in the following diagram (5 points each answer):**

    ____ Continental shelf   ____ Abyssal plain   ____ Seamount   ____ Island

    ____ Continental slope   ____ Trench   ____ Guyot   ____ Continent

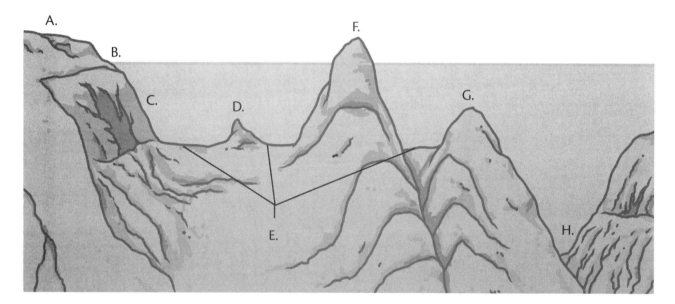

Below, label each ocean zone. Write each plant or animal from the list below next to the zone in which you are most likely to find it. (6 points each answer)

Shark	Tubeworms	Sea spider	Seaweed
Octopus	Anglerfish	Bioluminescent fish	Sea lilies
Algae	Coral	Jellyfish	Sponges

2. 0 to 660 feet is the _____ zone. _____

3. 660 to 3300 feet is the _____ zone. _____

4. 3300 to 13,200 feet is the _____ zone. _____

5. 13,200 feet and deeper is called the _____. _____

6. Very deep canyons are called _____. _____

Challenge questions

Mark each statement as either True or False (10 points each answer):

7. _____ Astronauts primarily study conditions under the ocean.

8. _____ Researchers can live in the *Aquarius* underwater lab for long periods of time.

9. _____ Researchers in *Aquarius* must undergo a decompression period before surfacing.

10. _____ Ocean trenches are found in subduction zones.

11. _____ Ocean trenches and ridges are found in the same areas.

12. _____ The Mariana Trench is the lowest place on earth.

13. _____ Most volcanic activity takes place on land.

14. _____ Ocean vents are usually located near underwater volcanoes.

15. _____ Coral reefs have been proven to be hundreds of thousands of years old.

16. _____ Coral reefs can grow very rapidly.

God's Design: Heaven & Earth Our Weather & Water	Final Exam	Scope: Lessons 1–34	Total score: ____of 100	Name	

Our Weather & Water

Fill in the blank with the correct term from below (5 points each answer):

Climate	Meteorology	Clouds	Equator
Air masses	Ice Age	Computer	
Sun	Precipitation	Glacier	

1. _____ is the study of the earth's atmosphere.

2. _____ is the average weather conditions in an area over a long period of time.

3. The Genesis Flood set up environmental conditions just right for a/an _____.

4. A/An _____ can form when snow does not completely melt in the summer.

5. Water vapor that condenses in the air forms _____.

6. Water that falls from the sky is called _____.

7. The _____ is responsible for most of the winds we experience on earth.

8. Hurricanes can only form near the _____.

9. The _____ is the most important piece of equipment for analyzing weather.

10. Weather fronts form where two _____ meet.

Analyze the weather station model and fill in the blanks (2 points each answer):

11. Temperature: _____

12. Wind speed: _____

13. Wind direction: _____

14. Precipitation: _____

15. Cloud cover: _____

16. Air pressure: _____

32
**
25

201

Mark each statement as either True or False (2 points each answer):

17. _____ Relative humidity is the total amount of water vapor in the air.

18. _____ Meteorologists use computers to help them forecast the weather.

19. _____ The oceans play an important role in the weather.

20. _____ El Niño is a wind in South America.

21. _____ The ocean contains many minerals and gases in addition to water.

22. _____ Ocean currents are sometimes a result of different amounts of salt in the water.

23. _____ Energy from waves can be used to make electricity.

24. _____ Waves are always helpful.

25. _____ Tides are lower when the sun and the moon line up.

26. _____ Most plants and animals are found in the twilight zone of the ocean.

Match the term with its definition (2 points each answer):

27. _____ Very deep valley in the ocean floor.   A. Pacific Ocean

28. _____ Very hot water coming up through sea floor.   B. Trench

29. _____ Large collection of colonies of polyps.   C. Coral reef

30. _____ Vehicle for deep-sea exploration.   D. Rip current

31. _____ Animal that can glow in the dark.   E. Deep-sea vent

32. _____ Largest ocean on earth.   F. Bioluminescent

33. _____ Organism that produces most of the oxygen in the ocean.   G. Algae

34. _____ Strong current moving water from the shore to the open sea.   H. Submersible

35. _____ Area where most plants and animals live in the ocean.   I. Sunlit zone

Challenge questions (5 points each answer):

36. Use the following words to label the diagram of the atmosphere with the correct levels.

Stratosphere   Thermosphere   Troposphere   Mesosphere

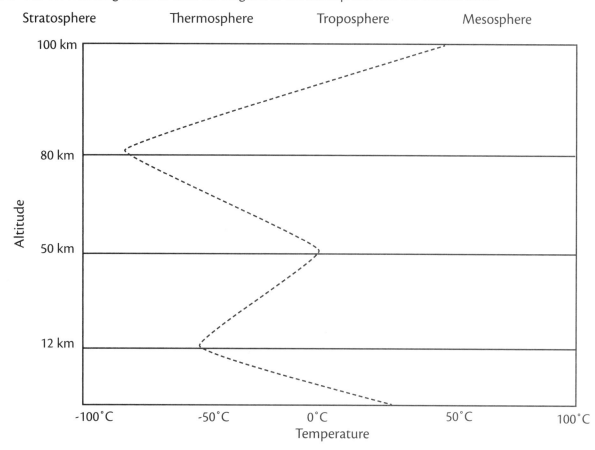

Short answer (10 points each answer):

37. What are the four "ingredients" needed to make weather? _____

_____

38. Explain how we get clues to what the climate was like in the past. _____

_____

39. List three kinds of fog. _____

40. What are two ways that acid rain can form? _____

_____

_____

41. The jet stream is most affected by the difference in temperature between which areas of the world? _____

_____

42. Name two kinds of radar that are used to detect severe weather. _____

_____

43. Explain how someone outside in wintertime could feel more comfortable in a colder temperature than he or she does when the outside temperature is warmer.

_____

_____

44. What are two methods for desalinating ocean water? _____

_____

Astronomy Quizzes and Final Exam

for Use with

Our Universe

(*God's Design: Heaven & Earth*)

Space Models & Tools

Short answer (8 points each answer):

1. What are the two ways the earth moves in space? _____

2. Why does the earth experience seasons? _____

3. Why are seasons an indication of God's provision for man? _____
   _____

4. What was the main idea of the geocentric model? _____
   _____

5. What is the main idea of the heliocentric model? _____
   _____

Mark each statement either True or False (6 points each answer):

6. _____ Scientists can prove where the earth came from.

7. _____ Scientists have proven the big bang is true.

8. _____ The Bible can tell us some things about astronomy.

9. _____ The Bible can tell us everything about astronomy.

10. _____ Gravity is the force that holds all planets in orbit.

11. _____ Galileo invented the first telescope.

12. _____ Heavier objects exert more gravity than lighter objects.

13. _____ Closer objects exert more gravity than ones farther away.

14. _____ The sun exerts more gravity on us than the earth does.

15. _____ The Bible says that God's power can be seen in His creation.

Challenge questions

Short answer (20 points each answer):

16. List at least one contribution that each of the following men made to the study of astronomy.

Nicolaus Copernicus _____

_____

Galileo _____

_____

Sir Isaac Newton _____

_____

17. Why do scientists look for ways to make telescopes larger? _____

_____

18. Explain briefly how the mirror of the Keck telescope is made. _____

_____

Outer Space

Match the term with its definition (5 points each answer):

1. _____ Millions of stars rotating around a center.

2. _____ Name of our galaxy.

3. _____ Collection of planets orbiting the sun.

4. _____ A group of stars that form a picture.

5. _____ Star that doesn't move with respect to the earth's rotation.

6. _____ Unit of measurement for distances in space.

7. _____ An exploding star.

8. _____ Cloud of gas and dust in space.

9. _____ Scientific study of the universe/space.

10. _____ Superstitious belief that stars control the future.

11. _____ Gap between Mars and Jupiter.

12. _____ Ball of ice that orbits the sun.

13. _____ Piece of space debris that reaches the earth's surface.

14. _____ Piece of space debris that burns up in the atmosphere.

15. _____ What you can tell from a star's color.

A. Light-year

B. North Star

C. Galaxy

D. Asteroid belt

E. Nova

F. Solar system

G. Comet

H. Nebula

I. Constellation

J. Meteorite

K. Astronomy

L. Milky Way

M. Astrology

N. Surface temperature

O. Meteor

Short answer (5 points each answer):

16. If a star has a blue color, is it hotter or cooler than our sun? _____

17. What **two** things do we need to know to determine how far away a star is?

_____   _____

18. Why do stars appear to move through the night sky? _____

19. Explain how the number of meteorites found in fossil layers confirms that the earth is young. _____

_____

Challenge questions

Short answer (10 points each answer):

20. Where do many evolutionists believe new stars are formed? Why is this unlikely? _____

_____

21. What names are given on a star map for the lines that are projected from the equator and the prime meridian?

_____

22. What is the most common evolutionary explanation for the origins of the universe? _____

_____

_____

23. Give one possible explanation for the ability to see distant starlight in a young world. _____

_____

_____

24. What is a group of asteroids traveling in the same path called? _____

25. Name **three** asteroids in the Trojan family. _____

_____ _____

26. Why does the existence of short-period comets indicate that the universe is young?_____

_____

_____

_____

27. What is the most likely explanation for the extinction of dinosaurs? _____

_____

_____

_____

Sun & Moon

List the planets in our solar system in order from the closest to the sun outward (4 points each answer):

_____

_____

Mark each statement as either True or False (4 points each answer):

1. _____ A lunar eclipse occurs when the moon blocks the light from the sun.

2. _____ The energy from the sun is generated by a process similar to a hydrogen bomb.

3. _____ Scientists can directly view the interior of the sun.

4. _____ The aurora borealis is a result of sunspots.

5. _____ A total solar eclipse causes the whole earth to become dark.

6. _____ Animals may act like night is falling during a solar eclipse.

7. _____ It is very dangerous to look at the sun even during a total eclipse.

8. _____ Solar collectors work best if they are painted glossy white.

9. _____ Solar cells convert the sun's rays into electricity.

10. _____ The same side of the moon always faces the earth.

11. _____ Maria are areas on the moon filled with water.

12. _____ The moon does not generate its own light.

Fill in the blank with the correct term (4 points each answer):

13. The moon is called a/an _____ moon when it is on the opposite side of the earth from the sun.

14. The moon is called a/an _____ moon when it is on the same side of the earth as the sun.

15. The main elements found in the sun are _____ and _____.

16. The _____ Theory for the origin of the moon says that it originally orbited the sun but was dislodged and later came to orbit the earth.

Challenge questions

Match the term with its definition (7 points each answer):

17. _____ Squashed circle.

18. _____ Place in orbit closest to the sun.

19. _____ Place in orbit farthest from the sun.

20. _____ Center of a sunspot.

21. _____ Outer edge of a sunspot.

22. _____ Not concentrated.

23. _____ Plain filled with hardened basalt.

24. _____ Depression made by a meteorite.

25. _____ Valley on the moon.

26. _____ Side of the moon facing the earth.

27. _____ Side of the moon facing away from the earth.

28. _____ Side of the moon facing away from the sun.

A. Near side

B. Ellipse

C. Perihelion

D. Penumbra

E. Dispersed

F. Maria

G. Aphelion

H. Dark side

I. Rill

J. Umbra

K. Crater

L. Far side

Short answer (8 points each answer):

29. Explain why sunspots near the sun's equator move faster than the ones near the poles.

30. List one problem that engineers must overcome in order to make solar energy more effective.

Planets

1. Describe each planet (and dwarf planet) by filling in the chart below. You may look at the lessons to find the answers. (Each box worth 2 points each.)

Planet	Terrestrial or Jovian	Atmosphere (Yes/No) If yes, what is it made of?	# of known moons	Rings (Yes/No)	Surface temperature (Hot/Cold/Comfortable)
Mercury					
Venus					
Earth					
Mars					
Jupiter					
Saturn					
Uranus					
Neptune					
Pluto (dwarf planet)					

Short answer (10 points):

2. If you could visit any of the planets, which would you choose and why?

_____

_____

_____

Challenge questions (25 points each answer):

Space probes have been invaluable in helping us understand the planets in our solar system. Choose three planets and list something that was discovered about them by using space probes.

1. _____

2. _____

3. _____

Short answer (5 points each answer):

4. Name **two** dwarf planets besides Pluto. _____   _____

Short answer (15 points):

5. Explain why planets that are closer to the sun orbit more quickly than those that are farther away.

_____

_____

_____

_____

Space Program

Choose the best answer for each question (6 points each answer):

1. _____ At this time, what is the best way to study long-term effects of zero gravity?

   A. Colonize the moon   B. Space station   C. Space shuttle   D. Vomit comet

2. _____ Which characteristic is generally not a quality of an astronaut?

   A. Lazy   B. Intelligent   C. Hard working   D. Interested in science

3. _____ What was designed to protect astronauts in space?

   A. Space probes   B. Space aliens   C. Space satellites   D. Space suits

4. _____ What wartime invention led to space exploration?

   A. Jeep   B. Tank   C. Rocket   D. Hand grenade

5. _____ What object was launched into space on Oct. 4, 1957?

   A. Sputnik   B. Sky Lab   C. Mir   D. Hubble telescope

6. _____ Who was the first man in space?

   A. John Glenn   B. Yuri Gagarin   C. Neil Armstrong   D. Alan Shepherd

7. _____ Who challenged America to put a man on the moon before 1970?

   A. Ronald Reagan   B. Jules Verne   C. John F. Kennedy   D. Wernher von Braun

8. _____ Which of the following is not a function of space satellites?

   A. Visiting planets   B. Taking pictures   C. Collecting data   D. Communication

9. _____ Which of the following programs did not help to put a man on the moon?

   A. Mercury   B. Gemini   C. Apollo   D. Space shuttle

10. _____ What rocket was used in the Apollo space program?

    A. Titan   B. Saturn V   C. Neptune   D. Jupiter

11. _____ Who was the first person to walk on the moon?

    A. Buzz Aldrin   B. John Glenn   C. Neil Armstrong   D. Michael Collins

12. _____ Which of the following was not left on the moon?

    A. Plaque   B. Footprints   C. CD player   D. American flag

13. _____ What shape was the shuttle orbiter?

    A. Square   B. Rectangular   C. Round   D. Triangular

14. _____ What was the maximum number of crew members on the space shuttle?

    A. 5   B. 7   C. 3   D. 10

Short answer (16 points):

15. Choose one of the astronauts you have learned about and explain what you admire about him/her.

    _____

Challenge questions

Short answer (10 points each answer):

16. List **three** ways that NACA helped improve flight.

    _____

    _____

    _____

17. List **three** challenges unique to living and working in space.

    _____

    _____

    _____

18. Why is private space research important? _____

    _____

    _____

19. What is the purpose of the Orion spacecraft? _____

    _____

    _____

20. In what ways is the Orion system similar to the Apollo system?_____

    _____

    _____

21. What is one fascinating thing you have learned?_____

    _____

    _____

God's Design: Heaven & Earth	Final	Scope:	Total score:	Name
Our Universe	Exam	Lessons 1–34	____of 100	

Our Universe

Fill in the blank with the correct term from below (3 points each answer):

Nebula	Supernova	Black hole	Eclipse
Asteroid	Comet	Meteor	Meteorite
Corona	Chromosphere	Photosphere	Atmosphere
Maria	Satellite	Probes	Solar energy

1. A/An _____ is a chunk of rock in a regular orbit around the sun.

2. The surface of the moon is covered with dark areas called _____.

3. A piece of space debris that burns up in the earth's atmosphere is a/an _____.

4. Space _____ can explore areas that man cannot.

5. A piece of space debris that hits the earth's surface is a/an _____.

6. A/An _____ is a star that experiences a very large explosion.

7. A/An _____ is a ball of ice and dust that orbits the sun.

8. A star that has exploded and collapsed in on itself is called a/an _____.

9. A/An _____ occurs when one heavenly body blocks the light from another heavenly body.

10. The gases surrounding a planet are its _____.

11. A large cloud of gas and dust in space is a/an _____.

12. Heated plasma that extends from the surface of the sun to 6,200 miles is the _____.

13. The _____ is the outermost part of the sun's atmosphere.

14. The visible surface of the sun is called the _____.

15. _____ is energy from the sun.

16. A/An _____ is anything that has a regular orbit around a planet.

Short answer (4 points each answer):

17. List at least one unique characteristic for each planet (and dwarf planet).

Mercury   Saturn

Venus   Uranus

Earth   Neptune

Mars   Pluto

Jupiter

Short answer (2 points each answer):

18. Describe why gravity is important to our solar system. _____

_____

19. Place these colors of stars in order from coolest to hottest: blue, orange, yellow, white._____

_____

20. What are the two ways that planets move through space? _____

_____

21. List three tools used to study space. _____

_____

22. What was the purpose of the Apollo missions? _____

_____

23. Why was the space shuttle developed? _____

_____

24. What is the purpose of the International Space Station? _____

_____

25. List three purposes of a space suit. _____

_____

Challenge questions

Mark each statement as either True or False (5 points each answer):

26. _____ A Foucault pendulum demonstrates the rotation of the earth.

27. _____ Kepler was the first to suggest the heliocentric model of the universe.

28. _____ Distant starlight proves the universe is billions of years old.

29. _____ The celestial equator on a star map corresponds to the equator on a map of the earth.

30. _____ Sir Isaac Newton improved on Galileo's design of the early telescope.

31. _____ The larger the opening of a telescope, the more you can magnify the image.

32. _____ Hektor and Achilles are two asteroids in the Trojan asteroid family.

33. _____ Science has proven that a meteor led to the extinction of the dinosaurs.

34. _____ Kepler's laws of planetary motion explain why planets move in ellipses.

35. _____ Solar flares are unrelated to sunspots.

36. _____ All planets are at the same tilt with respect to the sun.

37. _____ There are four Jovian and four terrestrial planets.

38. _____ Mercury and Venus have very different atmospheres from earth.

39. _____ More space probes have gone to Mars than to any other planet.

40. _____ SpaceShipOne proved that private space research is unrealistic.

41. _____ Orion is being modeled after the Apollo program.

42. _____ Only official astronauts are allowed on the International Space Station.

43. _____ Most astronauts have had a military background.

44. _____ The International Space Station was assembled in Florida.

45. _____ *Apollo 13* astronauts used ingenuity to solve problems in space after an explosion.

Earth Science Quizzes and Final Exam

for Use with

Our Planet Earth

(*God's Design: Heaven & Earth*)

Origins & Glaciers

Mark each statement as either True or False (4 points each answer):

1. _____ We can rely on the Bible to tell us the truth about God and His creation.

2. _____ We can prove scientifically where the earth came from.

3. _____ Science can answer all of our questions.

4. _____ Fossils have been located in every part of the world.

5. _____ The biblical account of the Flood explains much of what we see on earth.

6. _____ A scientist should disregard evidence that contradicts his/her theories.

7. _____ Scientists have not proven evolution to be true.

8. _____ The abundance of aquatic fossils is consistent with a worldwide flood.

9. _____ The worldwide Flood was God's punishment for man's sin.

10. _____ Evolutionists cannot adequately explain how conditions formed to create an ice age.

Short answer (4 points each answer):

11. List **three** biblical events that greatly affected the surface of the earth. _____

_____   _____

12. Describe **three** attributes of the earth that make it just right for life to occur here. _____

_____   _____

13. List **three** ways that geology affects your life. _____

_____   _____

14. List the **two** climate conditions required for an ice age.

_____   _____

15. List the **four** main studies of earth science.

_____   _____

_____   _____

Challenge questions

Short answer (10 points each answer):

16. Explain what the following quote is saying about scientists who believe in evolution.

    "Even if all the data points to an intelligent designer, such an hypothesis is excluded from science because it is not naturalistic."
    —Dr. Scott Todd, an immunologist at Kansas State University

    _____

    _____

    _____

17. Based on what you have learned about the Ice Age, in which areas would you expect to see evidence of glaciers? Write "yes" if you would expect to see it and "no" if you would not expect to see it.

    A. _____ Canada   D. _____ Norway

    B. _____ Montana   E. _____ Siberia

    C. _____ Mexico   F. _____ Egypt

18. List **three** economic or social effects caused by the Little Ice Age.

    a. _____

    b. _____

    c. _____

Rocks & Minerals

Choose the best answer for each question (6 points each answer):

1. _____ What percentage of all fossils are fossilized dinosaur bones?

   A. 50%   B. Less than 0.0001%   C. 1%   D. 5%

2. _____ What rock is commonly used for buildings and monuments?

   A. Granite   B. Sandstone   C. Limestone   D. Mica

3. _____ Which of the following is required in order for a plant or animal to fossilize?

   A. Millions of years   B. Humans   C. Be covered quickly   D. Rain

4. _____ What rock is made from the same element as diamonds?

   A. Coal   B. Quartz   C. Feldspar   D. Shale

5. _____ Why should we be careful when using the results of carbon-14 dating?

   A. Can be radioactive   B. Unreliable   C. Don't need to be   D. Silly

6. _____ What is one common characteristic of metamorphic rock?

   A. Soft   B. Round   C. Hard   D. Sticky

7. _____ How many elements are in a native mineral?

   A. 1   B. 10   C. 2 or more   D. 3

8. _____ What is a common mineral found in the human body?

   A. Gold   B. Calcium   C. Lead   D. Plutonium

9. _____ Which of the following is a native mineral?

   A. Salt   B. Baking Soda   C. Mud   D. Copper

10. _____ How are artificial gems easily identified?

   A. Less durable   B. Too perfect   C. Smaller crystals   D. A, B, and C

Short answer (10 points each answer):

11. Where is the earth's crust the thickest? _____

12. Name the three types of rocks. Describe how each type is formed and give an example of each.

A. _____

B. _____

C. _____

Challenge questions

Match the term with its definition (7 points each answer):

13. _____ Most common element in the earth's crust.

A. Porphyritic

14. _____ Most common rock in continental crust.

B. Breccia

15. _____ Most common rock in oceanic crust.

C. Oxygen

16. _____ Holes found in igneous rocks.

D. Native element

17. _____ Rock containing two or more sizes of crystals.

E. Granite

18. _____ Fragmental rock with rounded clasts.

F. Compound

19. _____ Fragmental rock with angular clasts.

G. Basalt

20. _____ Fossilized animal dung.

H. Vesicles

21. _____ Mineral with atoms of only one type.

I. Conglomerate

22. _____ Mineral with two or more elements in definite proportions.

J. Coprolites

23. _____ Order of rock layers according to evolutionists.

K. Gastroliths

24. _____ Smooth stones found inside fossilized animal bodies.

L. Geologic column

Short answer (3 points each answer):

25. What are **three** sources for moon rocks that are now on earth? _____

_____   _____

Short answer (7 points):

26. What is the difference between a rock and a mineral? _____

_____

_____

God's Design: Heaven & Earth Our Planet Earth	Quiz 3	Scope: Lessons 19–26	Total score: ____of 100	Name

Mountains & Movement

Match the term with its definition (6 points each answer):

1. _____ Theory that the crust is composed of several large landmasses.

2. _____ Name given to original landmass.

3. _____ Series of mountain peaks in a given area.

4. _____ Highest mountain peak on earth.

5. _____ Center of earthquake activity.

6. _____ Smaller quakes after a major earthquake.

7. _____ The Richter scale measures this.

8. _____ Instrument for measuring earthquakes.

9. _____ Blobs of lava that harden in the air.

10. _____ Volcano that has not erupted in the past 50 years.

11. _____ Volcano that is not expected to erupt again.

12. _____ Volcano that recently erupted in Washington State.

13. _____ Volcano that had one of the largest eruptions ever.

14. _____ Type of volcano formed from lava and solid material.

15. _____ One tectonic plate sliding under another.

A. Subduction

B. Dormant

C. Rodinia

D. Seismograph

E. Focus

F. Plate tectonics

G. Mount St. Helens

H. Mountain range

I. Mt. Everest

J. Krakatoa

K. Composite

L. Aftershocks

M. Extinct

N. Magnitude

O. Bombs

Short answer (10 points):

16. Explain the difference between the elevation of a mountain and its actual height. _____

_____

_____

Challenge questions

Mark each statement as either True or False (10 points each answer):

17. _____ Continental drift is the name given to the movement of tectonic plates.

18. _____ Rifting occurs when two tectonic plates collide.

19. _____ There are relatively few mountain ranges in the world.

20. _____ Pressure on tectonic plates can cause rocks to fold or bend.

21. _____ An anticline is formed when rocks bend upward.

22. _____ A hanging wall is the rock layers below a fault.

23. _____ A hanging wall moves downward in a normal fault.

24. _____ Most earthquakes and volcanoes are located around the Atlantic Ocean.

25. _____ Continental flood basalts are an indication of catastrophic plate movement in the past.

26. _____ Scientists cannot accurately predict when a volcano will erupt.

Water & Erosion

Fill in the blank with the correct term from below (6 points each answer):

Old Faithful	Column	Frost heaving	Gravity
Weathering	Fumarole	Landslide	Mass wasting
Geothermal	Moving water	Ash	Geyser
Limestone	Humus	Hydrogen sulfide	

1. A thermal feature that shoots hot water many feet into the air is a/an _____.

2. _____ is one of the most famous geysers in the world.

3. _____ energy can be obtained from areas containing geysers.

4. Geysers often contain _____, which gives them a bad smell.

5. A/An _____ is produced when super-heated steam reaches the surface.

6. The process of wearing down rocks is called _____.

7. _____ is the process that brings rocks to the surface each winter.

8. _____ is the effect of gravity pulling soil and rocks down a hill.

9. Rapid movement of large amounts of rocks and soil is called a/an _____.

10. The most powerful eroding force is _____.

11. The most important component of soil for growing plants is _____.

12. _____ can become fertile soil after a volcanic eruption.

13. A formation in a cave that goes from floor to ceiling is called a/an _____.

14. _____ is the force that causes water to move rapidly down a hill.

15. _____ is the main type of rock from which caves are formed.

Short answer (10 points):

16. Explain the process that causes a geyser to erupt. _____

_____

Challenge questions

Short answer (10 points each answer):

17. Where is the most likely place to find geothermal areas? _____

_____

18. List two types of chemical erosion. _____

_____

19. Which is more easily eroded: iron or rust? _____

_____

20. Where are rock glaciers likely to be located? _____

_____

21. What is a fossil rock glacier? _____

_____

22. Which has more power to erode: fast-moving water or slow-moving water? _____

_____

23. What is porosity in soil? _____

_____

24. What is permeability of soil? _____

_____

25. Why are porosity and permeability important? _____

_____

26. What are two indications of a large-scale flood found in Grand Canyon? _____

_____

Our Planet Earth

Label this diagram of the earth (2 points each answer):

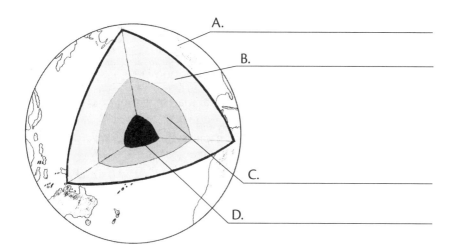

A. _____

B. _____

C. _____

D. _____

Mark each statement as either True or False (3 points each answer):

1. _____ Scientists "see" beneath the crust of the earth using earthquake (seismic) waves.

2. _____ The core is the coolest part of the earth.

3. _____ Magma is liquid rock under the surface of the earth.

4. _____ Coal is not a rock because it is organic.

5. _____ Rocks never change form.

6. _____ Rocks are made from one or more minerals or organic materials.

7. _____ Larger crystals form in igneous rock if it is cooled slowly.

8. _____ All rocks sink in water.

9. _____ Sandstone is a sedimentary rock.

10. _____ Limestone frequently contains fossils.

11. _____ Fossils prove that evolution is true.

12. _____ Fossils prove that creation is true.

13. _____ Natural gas is almost always found near oil deposits.

14. _____ Metamorphic rock can form at low temperatures.

Fill in the blank with the correct term from below (3 points each answer):

Uniformitarianism	1st law of thermodynamics	2nd law of thermodynamics
Erosional	Tsunami	Depositional
Evolutionists	Height	Earthquake
Elevation	Glacier	Indonesia

15. The _____ states that matter cannot be created or destroyed.

16. The _____ states that all systems tend toward a state of chaos.

17. Most _____ believe that everything in nature happened only by natural processes.

18. _____ is the belief that everything was formed by the slow processes we observe today.

19. A/An _____ is a thick sheet of ice that does not completely melt each summer.

20. _____ mountains are formed as wind and water erode material away.

21. _____ mountains are formed as layers of sediment are deposited.

22. One of the most dangerous side effects of an earthquake is a/an _____.

23. When stress due to moving tectonic plates is released it often causes a/an _____.

24. _____ is one of the most active volcanic countries in the world.

25. The difference between the base and the peak of a mountain is its _____.

26. The difference between sea level and the peak of a mountain is its _____.

Short answer (2 points each answer):

27. List two methods used by farmers to reduce soil erosion. _____

28. The evolutionist view of Grand Canyon is _____ of time, _____ of water.

29. The creationist view of Grand Canyon is _____ of time, _____ of water.

30. Describe the process for the eruption of a geyser. _____

_____

_____

31. Explain how water can break a rock. _____

_____

_____

Challenge questions

Match the term with its definition (6 points each answer):

32. _____ Lithification

33. _____ Clasts

34. _____ Matrix

35. _____ Striations

36. _____ Terminal morain

37. _____ Glacial erratic

38. _____ Syncline

39. _____ Foot wall

40. _____ Hanging wall

41. _____ Oxidation

42. _____ Porosity

43. _____ Permeability

A. Process which turns sediment into sedimentary rock.

B. Scratches made in the ground by a moving glacier.

C. Debris pushed ahead of a glacier.

D. Downward formation due to sideways pressure.

E. Fragments of rock cemented together.

F. Rock above a fault.

G. Chemical reaction involving bonding with oxygen.

H. Very large boulders moved by a glacier.

I. Measure of the pores or air spaces in soil.

J. Material cementing sedimentary rock particles.

K. The rate at which water flows through soil.

L. Rock below a fault.

Short answer (14 points each answer):

44. Explain how Mount St. Helens provides evidence that supports the Bible. _____

    _____

    _____

45. Explain how Grand Canyon provides evidence that supports the Bible. _____

    _____

    _____

Worksheet Answer Keys

for Use with

God's Design: Heaven & Earth

Our Weather & Water ━● *Worksheet* Answer Keys

1. A Christian View of Weather

What did we learn?

1. Is there a Christian view of weather? **Yes, there is a Christian view of everything. Either the weather is only naturalistic, or it is a result of a system designed by God the Creator.**

2. What three events described in the Bible have greatly affected the weather on earth? **Creation, the Curse due to the Fall of man, and the Flood.**

3. List three things you can learn about the weather from a newspaper weather report. **Actual high and low temperatures, predicted high and low temperatures, precipitation amounts, weather front locations, record high and low temperatures, weather conditions across the country.**

Taking it further

1. Why is it important to have a Christian view of weather? **It allows us to recognize God's handiwork.**

2. What are some geographical or physical characteristics that affect the weather in a particular area? **Large bodies of water, mountains, deserts, latitude, altitude.**

2. Structure of the Atmosphere

What did we learn?

1. What are the two main components of air? **Nitrogen—78%, Oxygen—21%.**

2. What are the five levels of the atmosphere? **Troposphere, stratosphere, mesosphere, thermosphere, exosphere. The lesson also mentioned the ionosphere and magnetosphere.**

3. What are some ways that the atmosphere protects us? **It protects us from extreme temperatures, vacuums, solar radiation and meteors, and provides oxygen to breathe.**

Taking it further

1. How would the earth be different if there were a higher concentration of oxygen? **Fires would burn uncontrollably.**

2. What would happen if the nitrogen in the atmosphere was replaced with a more reactive element, such as carbon? **The carbon would combine with the oxygen and form carbon dioxide, making the air unbreathable.**

Challenge: Atmospheric Temperature

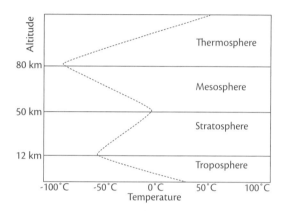

3. The Weight of Air

What did we learn?

1. What causes air to have weight? **Gravity pulling down on the air molecules.**

2. How much air pressure do we experience at sea level? **About 15 pounds per square inch.**

3. Why don't we feel the weight of the air molecules? **Our bodies push out with the same amount of pressure.**

4. Do you expect air pressure to be the same at all locations in the world? **No, as you go up in altitude, gravity exerts less force on the air molecules so there is less air pressure. Also, the pressure varies from one area to another causing weather fronts.**

Taking it further

1. Why is it important that air has weight? **The weight of the air allows us to have wind and moving air fronts.**

2. Why must aircraft be pressurized when flying at high altitudes? **The air pressure is much lower at high altitudes than it is on the ground and the lack of pressure can be painful for passengers, especially on their ears as they try to adjust to the lower pressure. If the pressure is low enough, there might not be enough oxygen to breathe.**

4. The Study of Weather

What did we learn?

1. What is meteorology? **The study of the atmosphere; particularly the study of the conditions of the troposphere.**

2. What are the five important conditions in the troposphere that meteorologists study? **Temperature, atmospheric/air pressure, humidity, wind, and precipitation.**

Taking it further

1. Why are meteorologists interested in studying the conditions of the troposphere? **They want to understand what affects the weather and be able to predict future weather conditions.**

2. How does the sun heat areas of the earth that do not receive much direct sunlight? **The sunlight is most concentrated in areas close to the equator. The air is warmer there than at the poles. However, because of air and water currents, warmer air and warmer water move toward the poles and cooler air and cooler water move toward the equator so the earth is more evenly heated.**

Challenge – Weather Ingredients worksheet

	Earth	Sun	Air	Water
W	Winter	Waves	Warm/Wind	Wet/White caps
E	Elevation	Eclipse	Expands	Evaporation
A	Absorbs	Angle	Atmosphere	Acid rain
T	Tilted axis	Temperature	Troposphere	Thunderstorm
H	Huge	Heat	Humidity	Hail/Humidity
E	Equator	Energy	Electricity	El Niño/Eye of storm
R	Rotation/Revolution	Radiation/Reflect	Relative humidity	Rain

5. Weather vs. Climate

What did we learn?

1. What is weather? **The atmospheric conditions present in an area at a given time.**

2. What is climate? **The average weather conditions for an area over a long period of time, including average temperatures and average precipitation.**

3. What are the five major climates found on earth? **Polar, desert, tropical, subtropical, and temperate.**

Taking it further

1. How does the Gobi Desert help create the monsoon? **The Gobi Desert heats the dry air around it. That air rises, allowing cooler air to move in. The cooler air comes from the Bay of Bengal and has a high moisture content, thus bringing rain to the area near the bay.**

2. Which of the following phrases describe weather and which describe climate?

   Cloudy with a chance of rain: **Weather.**

   Average of 20 inches of rain per year: **Climate.**

   Average summer temperature of 70°F: **Climate.**

   3 inches of snow in the past 24 hours: **Weather.**

6. Pre-Flood Climate

What did we learn?

1. Using clues from the Bible and science, what was the climate most likely like on earth before the Flood? **Warm; possibly no rain and more water vapor in the atmosphere; more constant temperature.**

Taking it further

1. How does the Bible say that plants were watered in the beginning? **The Bible says they were watered by springs and rivers. They were also probably watered by dew and from underground sources.**

2. How might the breaking of the earth's crust have contributed to the Flood? **Superheated water from inside the earth would have shot into the atmosphere and then rained back to earth.**

Challenge – Climate Clues worksheet

Clue #1:

1. Where do swamp cypress trees grow today? **Swampy areas in Georgia and Florida.**

2. What is the climate like in the Arctic Islands today? **Very cold and snowy.**

3. What possible explanation could there be for how the cypress tree fossils were formed in the Arctic Islands? **It may have been much warmer and wetter in the past so the trees could grow there, or the cypress trees were carried there from another location and then fossilized.**

Clue #2:

1. Where do hippopotami live today? **In grasslands where there is still water or in forests in Africa.**

2. What kind of plant life is required to support elephants? **An elephant eats 200–400 pounds of grass and other plants each day.**

3. Do many people live in villages in the Sahara Desert today? **Although there are some villages, most people that live in the desert are nomads.**

4. What can you conclude about the climate in the Sahara area before the Flood? **There must have been a lot more water and grass to support the life that was there.**

Clue #3:

1. What is the climate like in Antarctica today? **It is very cold and snowy—mostly frozen.**

2. What kind of plant life is required to support dinosaurs? **It depends on what kind of dinosaurs they were; they either ate plants or they ate the animals that ate the plants.**

3. What kind of plant life exists in Antarctica today? **There is very little plant life there.**

4. What can you conclude about the climate in Antarctica before the Flood? **It was probably much warmer than it is now.**

7. Climate Changes Due to the Genesis Flood

What did we learn?

1. What was the earth's climate like before the Flood? **Probably more uniformly warm and tropical.**

2. What was the climate like after the Flood? **It was much cooler and wetter than today. Ice covered much of the earth. It was still temperate in the areas near the equator.**

3. Approximately how much of the world was covered with ice during the Ice Age? **30%.**

4. What two weather conditions are necessary for an ice age to form? **Cool summers and wet/snowy winters.**

Taking it further

1. Why did God send a huge flood? **To destroy man because of his wickedness.**

2. What evidence points to a warmer pre-Flood climate? **Fossils of tropical plants around the world.**

3. What evidence points to an ice age? **Valleys cut by glaciers, frozen plants and animals, fossils in ice, etc.**

4. Do we see new glaciers forming today? **Yes, we see some new glaciers forming and some old glaciers growing bigger for a few years, but not on the large scale that occurred during the Ice Age.**

8. Global Warming

What did we learn?

1. What is global warming? **The increase in average temperature around the earth.**

2. What is the greenhouse effect? **Heat is trapped in the atmosphere and not released back into space.**

3. What is the main cause of the greenhouse effect? **Water vapor in the atmosphere.**

4. What amount of greenhouse effect is due to carbon dioxide in the atmosphere? **Only about 5%.**

5. How much has the temperature increased over the past 130 years? **Only about 1.2°F.**

6. Name at least two possible natural causes for increased temperatures. **Increased energy from the sun, decreased volcanic activity, increased cloud cover.**

Taking it further

1. Why is it important to know what assumptions are made when looking at computer models? **The assumptions greatly affect the outcome. If bad assumptions are made, then the results are unreliable.**

2. Ice core samples from Greenland indicate that rapid climate shifts have occurred in the past. How can your worldview affect the interpretation of this data?

If you believe the Bible you would expect to see rapid climate changes due to the Flood and its aftermath. If you believe in evolutionary processes and slow changes, this data can be very alarming and cause people to look for possible rapid climate changes in the future.

9. Water Cycle

What did we learn?

1. How does water vapor enter the atmosphere? **Through evaporation, transpiration, and vaporization.**

2. Which of these processes accounts for most of the water in the air? **Evaporation.**

3. How does water get from the atmosphere back to the earth? **Through precipitation such as rain, snow, sleet, dew, and hail.**

Taking it further

1. What are some factors that affect how fast the water evaporates from the surface of the ocean or lake? **Wind, heat, and the dryness of the air all affect the rate of evaporation.**

2. Why is it better to water your grass early in the morning rather than later in the day during the summer? **The air is hotter in the middle of the day and more of the water will evaporate and less will soak into the ground to help the grass grow.**

10. Cloud Formation

What did we learn?

1. What is a cloud? **A mass of water droplets or ice crystals suspended in the air.**

2. What is the dew point of air? **The point at which the air is holding the maximum amount of water for the current temperature.**

3. What is another name for dew point? **100% relative humidity.**

4. How do clouds form? **Warm, moist air rises. As it rises, it cools. Eventually it reaches the dew point and water condenses on dust and pollen particles to form clouds.**

Taking it further

1. Often, one side of a mountain range receives much more rain than the other side. Why do you think this happens? **If the winds come primarily from one direction, clouds will form more often on the near side of the mountain. As these clouds are forced to rise, they cool and can no longer hold all of the water, resulting in precipitation on that side of the mountain.**

2. Why don't clouds always result in rain? **If the air around a cloud is dry, the water in the cloud will evaporate again instead of raining.**

3. What role do pollen and dust play in cloud formation? **Water at dew point needs something on which to condense. Dust and pollen particles in the air provide this and thus encourage condensation and cloud formation.**

11. Cloud Types

What did we learn?

1. What are the two ways that clouds are classified? **By shape and altitude.**

2. What are the three main shapes of clouds and how does each look? **Stratus—stretched out layers; cumulus—heaped, piled up, and fluffy; cirrus—curly or wispy.**

3. What are rain clouds called? **Nimbus clouds.**

Taking it further

1. What would a fluffy cloud at 0.5 miles (0.8 km) be called? **Stratocumulus.**

2. What would a wispy cloud at 5 miles (8 km) above the earth be called? **Cirrus—it would be cirrus by shape and cirrus by altitude but would not be called cirrocirrus, just cirrus.**

Challenge questions – Fog formation

1. Why does fog form inside the bottle? **The air inside the bottle cooled and the water vapor condensed.**

2. Why do you think we have you put a match inside the bottle? **The smoke particles gave the water vapor something to stick to.**

12. Precipitation

What did we learn?

1. What are the main types of precipitation? **Dew, frost, drizzle, rain, sleet, hail, and snow.**

2. What is the difference between drizzle and rain? **Drizzle is very tiny drops; rain is water droplets larger than 0.02 inches (0.05 cm).**

3. What shape do snowflakes have? **Each is unique but they all have six sides—hexagonal.**

4. What is coalescence? **When water droplets begin to stick together to form bigger drops.**

5. What is the difference between sleet and hail? **Sleet is very small ice pellets, while hail is larger pellets of ice.**

Taking it further

1. What conditions are necessary for large hailstones to form? **Warm, humid conditions are needed to form the strong updrafts necessary to keep the ice pellets in the air long enough to become hail.**

2. How effective is cloud seeding? **No one really knows. Only clouds that are likely to produce rain are seeded, so it is impossible to tell if the rain was caused naturally or as a result of the seeding.**

13. Air Masses & Weather Fronts

What did we learn?

1. What is an air mass? **A large amount of air that has uniform temperature and humidity.**

2. How do air masses form? **When there is very little wind in an area, the air does not move around much and becomes uniform.**

3. How does the air pressure compare between warm and cold air masses? **Warm air masses usually have lower air pressure than cold air masses.**

Taking it further

1. How would a cold air mass that develops over land be classified? **A continental polar air mass.**

2. Why do most weather changes occur along weather fronts? **Air becomes very unsettled along a front. This allows air to heat up and cool down, which encourages precipitation. The air pressure, temperature, and**

humidity levels are different from one air mass to another, so when one air mass displaces another it will probably change the weather.

14. Wind

What did we learn?

1. What is the main cause of wind? **The sun heats the earth and air. Hot air rises and cooler air moves in to take its place.**

2. What is a jet stream? **A very fast moving current of air high in the atmosphere.**

3. What are trade winds? **Winds that consistently blow in a particular direction in an area of the ocean during a particular season.**

Taking it further

1. Why was it important for sailors of sailing ships to know about trade winds, doldrums, and other prevailing winds? **They could use the winds to help them sail faster, and they wanted to avoid the doldrums. Today's ships are not dependent on wind so this is not as big of an issue for shipping today as it used to be.**

2. Why does the breeze near the coast blow toward the land in the morning and toward the sea at night? **Land heats and cools faster than water so the air above the land heats faster than the air above the water during the day and cools faster after sunset.**

15. Thunderstorms

What did we learn?

1. What is a thunderstorm? **A large storm with high winds, lots of rain, thunder, and lightning.**

2. What causes lightning? **Water particles and ice crystals rub against each other creating ions. Positive ions collect at the top of the cloud and negative ions collect at the bottom. When these ions connect, energy is released in the form of light.**

3. What causes thunder? **Lightning heats the air, causing it to expand and then contract very quickly as it cools, which causes an explosive sound.**

Taking it further

1. Why does hail form in thunderstorms that have high clouds? **Higher clouds form when the air is moving more quickly up and down. At higher altitudes the water freezes, forming ice pellets and the faster moving air forces the pellets up into the cloud over and over, forming hail.**

2. Why do thunderstorms usually form on hot summer days? **The hotter the air, the more it will expand causing more updrafts and bigger clouds.**

Challenge – Flash floods

Things you can do to be safe in a severe thunderstorm include: Monitor the weather station when severe storms are likely so you have as much warning as possible. Seek shelter inside a house or other building. Stay away from water. Because of the electrical nature of lightning, avoid using the telephone or taking a shower during a severe storm and do not touch metal pipes, fences, or wires. Do not stand on a hilltop; avoid being the tallest object around if you are stuck outside. Get to higher ground if a flash flood is predicted.

16. Tornadoes

What did we learn?

1. What causes a tornado to develop? **Warm updrafts suck cool downdrafts into them. The falling drier air can cause the updraft to begin to spiral. If there is enough heat and energy, the spiral can tighten and speed up, resulting in a tornado.**

2. What is the difference between a funnel cloud and a tornado? **A funnel cloud does not touch the ground.**

3. What is a waterspout? **A tornado that develops over the water.**

4. When do most tornadoes occur in the United States? **In the springtime.**

Taking it further

1. How does the jet stream affect tornado formation? **The jet stream is a fast moving current of air at high altitudes. It can cause the air in a thunderstorm to move more quickly, adding energy to the storm. This encourages tornado formation.**

2. Why should you take shelter during a tornado? **The greatest threat to people during a tornado is flying debris. Taking shelter can protect you from the debris.**

17. Hurricanes

What did we learn?

1. What is a hurricane? **A huge storm that develops over warm waters.**

2. Where do most hurricanes occur? **In the western Pacific Ocean.**

3. What is the difference between a tropical depression, a tropical storm, and a hurricane? **Tropical depression has wind speeds of 25–38 mph; tropical storm has wind speeds of 39–73 mph; and a hurricane has wind speeds of at least 74 mph.**

Taking it further

1. Why does a hurricane dissipate once it reaches land? **The storm is fueled or energized by the warm, moist air of the tropical ocean. Once it reaches land, the energy to keep the storm going is no longer there.**

2. How does warm water help create and energize a hurricane? **The warm water easily evaporates and the warm air rises. As it rises, the air cools and the water condenses. The condensing water releases heat causing more water to evaporate setting up a cycle that can result in hurricane formation.**

Storm Word Scramble

1. When warm, moist air cools. **condensation**

2. A large amount of air with uniform temperature and humidity. **air mass**

3. Where two air masses meet. **front**

4. Air movements caused by the sun heating the ground more near the equator than at the poles. **global winds**

5. A very high, fast-moving current of air. **jet stream**

6. Phenomenon caused when ions discharge energy in a cloud. **lightning**

7. A spiraling cloud that does not touch the ground. **funnel cloud**

8. A tornado that forms over water. **waterspout**

9. A hurricane that forms in the Pacific Ocean. **typhoon**

10. Rising sea level in front of a hurricane. **storm surge**

11. Equipment used by National Weather Service to predict tornadoes and hurricanes. **Doppler radar**

12. Person who studies the weather. **meteorologist**

13. Location where 90% of hurricanes form. **Pacific Ocean**

14. Type of cloud found in thunderstorms. **cumulonimbus**

15. Instrument for indicating wind direction. **wind sock**

18. Gathering Weather Information

What did we learn?

1. What does a meteorologist measure with a thermometer? **Temperature of the air.**

2. What is air temperature? **A measure of the movement of air molecules indicating the energy they possess.**

3. What are the two temperature scales commonly used? **Fahrenheit and Celsius.**

4. What does a meteorologist measure with a barometer? **Air pressure.**

5. What is air pressure? **Pressure produced by the weight of air molecules.**

6. What does a meteorologist measure with a psychrometer? **Relative humidity.**

7. What is relative humidity? **The ratio of the amount of moisture in the air to the amount of moisture the air could hold at the current temperature.**

Taking it further

1. Why does a sling psychrometer give faster results than a stationary psychrometer? **The wet bulb of a sling psychrometer is exposed to dry air more quickly because of its movement, so water evaporates more quickly, giving a faster reading.**

2. Why do thermometers need to be kept out of direct sunlight? **The energy from the sun will directly heat the liquid in the thermometer and will give a higher reading than the air temperature around it.**

19. More Weather Instruments

What did we learn?

1. How do meteorologists measure wind? **An anemometer measures wind speed, and a wind sock or wind vane indicates wind direction.**

2. How do meteorologists measure weather at higher altitudes? **With weather balloons carrying radiosondes—boxes with weather instruments that transmit measurements back to the weather station.**

3. What sophisticated instruments do meteorologists use? **Radar, Doppler radar, satellites, and computers.**

Taking it further

1. Why is it important for a meteorologist to take weather readings at higher altitudes? **This gives him/her a picture of the entire weather system. It shows the size of air masses and it shows where weather fronts are occurring.**

2. Why might a weather satellite be useful for tracking a hurricane? **A satellite can show the whole storm as well as its path in relation to landmasses.**

3. Why are computers necessary for weather tracking and forecasting? **The amount of data needed to understand the weather is enormous. Computers can take all of that data and analyze it and print it in formats that are easier for people to read and understand.**

20. Reporting & Analyzing Weather Information

What did we learn?

1. What happens to the weather data collected at weather stations? **The information is sent to the National Weather Service where it is compiled and analyzed, and then used to generate weather charts and maps, and to make forecasts.**

2. Other than from land-based weather stations, where does the National Weather Service get weather information? **From airborne radiosondes, aircraft, ships, radar, and satellites.**

3. What group of the National Weather Service generates local severe thunderstorm and flash flood warnings? **Local Weather Forecasting Offices.**

Taking it further

1. Why is it necessary for one location to collect and analyze all of the weather data across the United States? **Air masses change the weather as they move across the country. It is necessary to know where the different air masses are, how big they are, and in what directions they are moving. This can only be obtained by compiling measurements from multiple locations.**

2. Why is a standard picture or model needed for reporting weather information? **God designed people to be able to quickly process pictures into information, so anyone looking at the model can immediately see the weather conditions in a particular area. This is faster and easier than a written description.**

3. Why must the information in the model be converted to electrical signals before it is transmitted to the National Weather Service's computer? **Computers only deal with electrical signals; pictures are for humans.**

Weather Station Model worksheet

1. How much of the sky is covered with clouds? **Complete cloud cover (100%).**

2. From which direction is the wind blowing? **Southwest.**

3. What is the wind speed? **15 knots.**

4. What is the current temperature? **78°F.**

5. Is any precipitation falling? If so, what kind? **Yes, rain.**

6. What is the current dew point? **40°F.**

7. What is the current air pressure? **1015.8 millibars .**

21. Forecasting the Weather

What did we learn?

1. How do meteorologists predict what the weather will be like? **Weather data from around the country and around the world is fed into a computer that generates weather forecasts for each area of the country. Local meteorologists use these forecasts as well as their own experience to predict what the weather will be like for the next several days.**

2. What is an important function of local National Weather Service offices? **They monitor weather conditions and put out warnings and alerts when dangerous weather conditions are likely to develop.**

3. Other than local weather forecasts, what types of weather forecasts are generated by the NWS? **Fire weather, airport weather (TAF), coastal weather forecast, offshore weather forecast, hurricane forecasts, and climate change forecasts.**

Taking it further

1. Why are weather forecasts more accurate today than they were 20 years ago? **New computer programs are able to compile more information and make better models of the weather, plus more information is available.**

2. Are weather forecasts always reliable? **No, the weather is very complicated and will never be fully understood. God is the only one who knows exactly what the weather will be.**

22. Weather Station: Final Project

What did we learn?

1. What does each instrument in your weather station measure? **Thermometer—temperature; psychrometer—relative humidity; wind sock—wind direction; anemometer—wind speed; barometer—air pressure; rain gauge—precipitation.**

Taking it further

1. Why might you want to have your own weather station? **It's fun and educational.**

2. Why might your weather readings be different from what is reported in the newspaper or on TV? **Your instruments are not as accurate and they are taking their measurements in a different location.**

3. Did you see any relationship between air pressure and wind and rain? **You most likely noticed that when the air pressure changed there was more wind. Also, lower air pressure indicates a warm front that usually has more moisture and is more likely to bring rain. Higher air pressure usually indicates a cold front that is likely to have drier air and is less likely to bring rain.**

4. What changes did you see in your temperature readings from day to day? **Answers will vary.**

23. Overview of the Ocean

What did we learn?

1. What are the names of the five oceans? **Pacific, Atlantic, Indian, Antarctic (or Southern), and Arctic.**

2. Which ocean is the largest? **The Pacific Ocean.**

3. How much of the earth is covered by the oceans? **About 71%.**

Taking it further

1. How do the oceans affect the weather? **The oceans change temperature more slowly than land, so winds are generated near the ocean. Also, the heat energy in the ocean fuels many storms including hurricanes. Oceans are where most evaporation takes place so they ultimately generate most precipitation.**

2. Why do some people say there is only one ocean? **All of the oceans are connected to each other so you could say there is only one ocean on earth.**

3. Why was the Indian Ocean the first ocean to have established trade routes? **The monsoon winds blow steadily in one direction for half the year and then blow in the other direction the other half of the year. This made it easy for ships to sail to particular areas during certain times of the year.**

24. Composition of Seawater

What did we learn?

1. What are the main elements found in the ocean besides water? **Salt, magnesium, and bromine.**

2. How does salt get into the ocean? **Water flowing over land dissolves salt and other minerals then leaves them behind in the oceans when the water evaporates.**

3. What is one gas that is dissolved in the ocean water? **Oxygen is the main gas; nitrogen, carbon dioxide, and other gases are present as well.**

Taking it further

1. Why is there more oxygen near the surface of the ocean than in deeper parts? **Phytoplankton and other plants grow near the surface and produce oxygen that dissolves in the water. Also, some oxygen dissolves into the water from the air.**

2. How does the saltiness of the ocean support the idea of a young earth? **If the earth were billions of years old, the amount of salt in the oceans would be much higher than it is today. The amount of salt in the ocean is consistent with an earth about 6,000 years old.**

25. Ocean Currents

What did we learn?

1. What is a surface ocean current? **A continuous movement of water in a particular direction on the surface of the ocean.**

2. What are the main causes of surface currents? **Heating from the sun and movement by the wind.**

3. How fast do surface currents usually move? **2–3 miles per hour.**

4. What is a subsurface ocean current? **A continuous movement of water in a particular direction under the surface of the ocean.**

5. What are the main causes of subsurface currents? **Differences in density of warmer and cooler water and differences in density of saltier and less salty water.**

Taking it further

1. What climate changes do warm surface currents cause? **Coastal areas near warm currents tend to be warmer and have milder winters.**

2. What climate changes do cool surface currents cause? **Coastal areas near cool currents tend to be drier than other areas, often resulting in deserts.**

3. Why do warm surface currents move away from the equator while cooler currents move toward the equator? **The sun shines more intensely at the equator so the water is warmed more there than at the poles; the wind then moves this warm water away from the equator.**

26. Waves

What did we learn?

1. How are waves generated? **Friction between the wind and the surface of the water picks up water and moves it a short distance. This adds energy to the surface of the ocean causing it to move in waves.**

2. How far does a particular water molecule move when a wave is generated? **Only a short distance, perhaps a few feet at most.**

3. What is the crest of a wave? **The crest is the highest part of the wave.**

4. What is the trough of a wave? **The trough is the lowest part of the wave.**

5. What are two ways to measure a wave? **Wave height—the difference between the crest and the trough, and wavelength—the distance between two crests.**

Taking it Further

1. Explain how a wave can move across the ocean without moving the water molecules across the ocean. **The individual molecules are moved a short distance by the wind. When they fall back down to the surface of the ocean they transfer their energy to other molecules that then move forward. Those molecules hit other molecules and so on until the wave dies or reaches the shore.**

2. What kind of a path does an individual water molecule take in a wave? **It is lifted by the wind, moves forward, falls down and is pushed back by other molecules—so it travels in a small circular path.**

3. Why does a wave get tall as it approaches the shore? **Friction causes the base of the wave to slow down when it hits the ocean floor. This pushes more water up, causing the wave to get taller and then break.**

4. Why are tsunamis such dangerous waves? **A tsunami is a wave that travels very fast and has a tremendous amount of energy. As it reaches the shore, it causes large amounts of water to pile up so that a giant wall of water hits the shore causing massive flooding.**

27. Tides

What did we learn?

1. What is a high tide? **When the water level is the highest along a shore.**

2. What causes the water level to change along the shore? **The gravitational pull of the moon and to a lesser extent the gravitational pull of the sun.**

3. How often does a high or low tide occur each day? **There are two high tides and two low tides each day, approximately six hours apart.**

Taking it further

1. Why does a spring tide only occur when there is a full moon or when there is a new moon? **This is the only time during the month when the sun is in a direct line with the earth and the moon, thus adding its gravitational pull to that of the moon.**

2. Since the sun is so much larger than the moon, why doesn't it have a greater effect on the tides than the moon? **Because the moon is much closer than the sun: 240,000 miles (386,000 km) vs. 93 million miles (150 million km).**

3. Where should you build your sandcastle if you don't want the water to knock it down? **Farther from the water than the highest point that the waves reach during high tide.**

Ocean Movements Word Search

I	P	M	C	B	E	I	Y	D	**N**	**E**	**A**	**P**	X	Z
C	B	R	**G**	R	A	I	F	C	E	K	P	L	U	Y
U	O	E	**R**	I	B	L	**I**	**M**	**A**	**N**	**U**	**S**	**T**	W
R	F	**W**	**A**	**V**	**E**	**L**	**E**	**N**	**G**	**T**	**H**	T	D	Q
R	H	F	**V**	**B**	**R**	**E**	**A**	**K**	**E**	**R**	F	I	E	E
E	K	L	I	N	J	I	E	**Y**	**L**	**O**	**W**	W	S	R
N	N	E	T	L	Y	R	E	**T**	V	U	C	S	**C**	E
T	D	E	**Y**	S	W	**H**	R	**I**	K	**G**	J	**G**	**R**	V
X	T	Z	**W**	**G**	O	U	**S**	N	**H**	V	F	**E**	L
M	N	H	**T**	**I**	**D**	**E**	L	**N**	F	T	V	N	**S**	O
V	C	K	**H**	**N**	I	H	U	**E**	I	**R**	**I**	**P**	**T**	B
R	E	D	S	**D**	H	I	J	**D**	K	L	D	E	V	D
C	A	F	E	H	U	**F**	**R**	**I**	**C**	**T**	**I**	**O**	**N**	N
I	D	I	**E**	**C**	**A**	**F**	**R**	**U**	**S**	**B**	**U**	**S**	U	X
V	G	I	J	K	Y	T	S	T	R	U	N	F	Q	O

28. Wave Erosion

What did we learn?

1. What causes erosion along a beach? **Waves; large waves from storms and tsunamis cause the most damage, but everyday waves cause erosion as well.**

2. What are some problems that can arise from wave erosion? **The changing shoreline can cause problems with buildings that are built too close to the shore. Also, sand that is moved from the shore can block bays and build up sand bars that block the movement of ships.**

3. What features have been formed along the shore by the erosion from waves? **Sea caves, arches, and columns of stone.**

Taking it further

1. Why don't shores completely erode if water is constantly pulling sand away from them? **Water is also bringing new sand and debris and depositing them as well.**

2. How can you protect your building from the damaging effects of tsunamis and other storm-generated waves? **Build further from the shore.**

Challenge – Erosional Land Formations worksheet

1. **Spit**
2. **Hook**
3. **Barrier island**
4. **Bay barrier**

29. Energy from the Ocean

What did we learn?

1. What are three ways that people are using the ocean to generate electricity? **Tidal barrages, wave towers and wave buoys, and heat exchangers.**

Taking it further

1. Why are tidal barrages used infrequently? **There are only a few places where there is a constant flow of water, and the barrages can damage the ecosystems.**

2. Why do heat exchangers have to be built near the equator? **They rely on a difference in water temperature. The water that is hundreds of feet below the surface is cold no matter where you are, but the surface waters are consistently warm only in tropical areas.**

3. Scientists hope to use the warm tropical waters to generate electricity. What natural weather phenomenon is fueled by these warm tropical waters? **Hurricanes, El Niño.**

30. Sea Exploration

What did we learn?

1. What invention in the 1940s allowed divers to more freely explore the ocean? **The Aqua-Lung—a portable air tank.**

2. How do oceanographers study the ocean today? **They scuba dive in relatively shallow water and they use submersibles and remotely operated vehicles to see what is in the deeper parts of the ocean.**

3. What special equipment do submersibles have? **They are specially designed to withstand great water pressure. They have video cameras, manipulator arms, and storage containers for samples. They also have communication equipment.**

Taking it further

1. Why does a submersible or ROV need headlights? **Below a few hundred feet (100 m), there is no sunlight and the water is very dark. Lights are needed so the scientists can see what is down there.**

2. Why can't scuba divers go very deep in the ocean? **The water pressure is too great for their bodies.**

3. How are submersibles similar to spacecraft? **They both provide protection to people from the surrounding environment by providing the right air pressure and by providing air to breathe. They both contain useful equipment that allows people to explore new areas.**

31. Geography of the Ocean Floor

What did we learn?

1. What are the three areas of the ocean floor? **The continental shelf, the continental slope, and the abyssal plain.**

2. What are some features of the abyssal plain? **There are relatively flat areas; there are seamounts, guyots, islands, and trenches.**

3. What is a guyot? **An underwater mountain with a flat top.**

Taking it further

1. What part of the ocean floor is most difficult to observe? **The trenches because they are so deep and have such great water pressure.**

2. What do you think is the most likely cause of seamounts? **Volcanic activity is believed to cause nearly all seamounts.**

32. Ocean Zones

What did we learn?

1. What are the five ocean zones? **Sunlit/euphotic zone, twilight/disphotic zone, midnight/aphotic zone, abyss, and trenches.**

2. What zone has the most life? **The sunlit zone.**

3. Where is the sunlit zone located? **Over the continental shelf, in the top 660 feet (300 m) of water.**

Taking it further

1. Why is all algae and plant life found in the sunlit zone? **Plants need sunlight to perform photosynthesis and grow, so they cannot live where no sunlight penetrates.**

2. Why are so few animals found in the very deepest parts of the ocean? **The water pressure is too great for most animals. Those that can withstand the pressure must live where there is sufficient food.**

Ocean Zones worksheet

1. **Sunlit zone**

2. **Twilight zone**

3. **Midnight zone**

4. **Abyss**

5. **Trench**

Plants and animals: Accept reasonable answers—see lesson for examples.

33. Vents & Smokers

What did we learn?

1. What is a deep-sea vent? **An area on the sea floor where very hot water shoots up from below the surface of the ocean floor.**

2. What provides the food source for the animals living near these vents? **A type of bacteria that thrives on the sulfur in the vent water.**

Taking it further

1. Why were scientists so surprised to find an ecosystem thriving near the deep-sea vents? **They believed that all life in the sea depended on the plants growing in the sunlit zone, but this ecosystem gets its food supply from the bacteria that grow in the hot water.**

2. Why can the water stay so hot near the vents without turning to steam? **The great pressure of the water at the depths in which the vents are found keeps the water in liquid form even at very high temperatures.**

34. Coral Reefs

What did we learn?

1. What is a coral? **A tiny animal that resembles an upside down jellyfish that lives in the ocean and secretes a hard cup around itself.**

2. What is a coral reef? **A large collection of coral all growing together.**

3. What are the three types of coral reefs? **Fringing reef, barrier reef, and atoll.**

Taking it further

1. Why are coral reefs only found in relatively shallow ocean water? **The algae inside the coral require sunlight to make food.**

2. Why might a coral reef be a hazard to ships? **A coral reef may not be visible from the surface but may be big enough to cause damage to the ship.**

3. What could happen to a coral reef if the water became cloudy or too warm for the algae to survive? **The algae would die and the coral may eventually die as well.**

Our Universe → *Worksheet* Answer Keys

1. Introduction to Astronomy

What did we learn?

1. What is astronomy? **The study of the stars, planets, moons, and other items in space.**

2. Why should we want to study astronomy? **To learn more about God's creation and see His glory.**

Taking it further

1. What is one thing you really want to learn during this study? **Answers will vary.**

2. Write your question or questions on a piece of paper and save it to make sure you find the answers by the end of the book. **Encourage the student to do this and keep it in an accessible place.**

God's Purpose For the Universe worksheet

1. I was designed to rule the day: **Sun/greater light**.

2. I was designed to rule the night: **Moon/lesser light**.

3. We are times that are to be marked by the movement of the sun, moon, and stars: **Seasons, days, and years.**

4. Besides marking times, I am another reason why the sun, moon, and stars were made: **To give light and to show signs.**

5. We were made by God's hands and this is what will eventually happen to us: **Heavens and earth will perish and wear out**.

6. This is higher than me (the earth): **The heavens.**

7. I am what you will see in the heavens in the last days: **Wonders, sun to darkness, moon to blood.**

8. I (the sun), stood still for this long, until Joshua and the Israelites defeated their enemies: **About a full day.**

Challenge – Knowledge of the Stars worksheet

1. What is the nearest star to the earth? **Sun.**

2. What are the main elements in stars? **Hydrogen and helium.**

3. What is the name of the galaxy that we live in? **Milky Way.**

4. What is special about Polaris, the North Star? **It does not appear to move through the sky like the other stars.**

5. What unit of distance is used to measure items in space? **Light year, parsec, or astronomical unit.**

6. What name describes when one celestial body blocks the light from another? **Eclipse.**

7. What force holds the planets in their places? **Gravity.**

8. Name three items found in space besides stars, moons, and planets. **Comets, asteroids, meteors, plutoids, space junk, satellites, space station.**

9. Name two scientists important to our understanding of astronomy. **Newton, Galileo, Copernicus, Kepler, Hubble.**

10. How long does it take for light to travel from the sun to the earth? **About 8 minutes.**

2. Space Models

What did we learn?

1. What are the two major models that have been used to describe the arrangement of the solar system? **Geocentric/Ptolemaic—earth centered, and Heliocentric/Copernican—sun centered.**

2. What was the main idea of the geocentric model? **The earth was the center of the universe and everything revolved around it.**

3. What is the main idea of the heliocentric model? **The sun is the center of the solar system and the earth and other planets revolve around it.**

4. What force holds all of the planets in orbit around the sun? **Gravity.**

Taking it further

1. Which exerts the most gravitational pull, the earth or the sun? **The sun because it is much more massive than the earth.**

2. If the sun has a stronger gravitational pull, then why aren't objects pulled off of the earth toward the sun? **The strength of the gravitational pull decreases with distance. The pull of the earth is stronger on us because we are so much closer to the center of the earth than we are to the sun. If an object moves far enough away from the earth, the earth's gravity no longer has much effect on it. And if that object moves close enough to the sun, it will be pulled into the sun by the sun's gravity.**

3. The Earth's Movement

What did we learn?

1. What are the two different types of motion that the earth experiences? **Rotation on its axis and revolution around the sun.**

2. What observations can we make that are the result of the rotation of the earth on its axis? **Day and night, the stars rotating in the sky, the bulging of the earth, diagonal air flow.**

3. What observations can we make that are the result of the revolution of the earth around the sun? **Changing of the seasons, parallax of stars, more meteors observed after midnight.**

4. What is a solstice? **The first day of summer or the first day of winter, when the earth is in the place in its orbit where the sun is hitting directly on either the Tropic of Cancer or the Tropic of Capricorn.**

5. What is an equinox? **The first day of spring or the first day of autumn, when the earth is halfway between the solstices.**

Taking it further

1. What are the advantages of the earth being tilted on its axis as it revolves around the sun? **This gives us seasons. Without this tilt, the temperatures would be relatively stable year round. This would result in less of the earth being able to grow crops. Only the warm areas near the equator would have warm enough weather to grow food.**

2. One argument against Copernicus's theory was that if the earth were moving, flying birds would be left behind. Why don't the birds get left behind as the earth moves through space? **The atmosphere in which the birds are flying moves with the earth because of gravity.**

Challenge questions – Foucault pendulum

1. What forces are affecting the pendulum? **Gravity is pulling down on the weight at the end of the pendulum, and air is resisting the movement of the pendulum.**

2. Why does the pendulum eventually stop moving? **Because of the air resistance.**

3. How does a Foucault pendulum keep moving for hours or days at a time without stopping? **They are often designed with an iron ring near the top where the pendulum is attached to the building. Also, there** are electromagnets placed around the ring. As the pendulum swings through a certain part of its arc the magnet turns on, attracting the ring. Then the magnet turns off to allow the pendulum to swing freely. This magnet system compensates for the air resistance that the pendulum experiences, so it does not slow down.

4. Tools for Studying Space

What did we learn?

1. What are the three main types of telescopes? **Refracting—using only lenses, Reflecting—using lenses and mirrors, Radio—collecting radio waves. Catadioptric and space telescopes are also acceptable answers.**

2. What was one disadvantage of the early refracting telescope? **The refracting lens bent the light causing false colors to appear around the edges of the image.**

3. How did Newton avoid this problem? **He used mirrors instead of a lens to collect the light.**

Taking it further

1. Why do you think scientists wanted to put a telescope in space? **It would give better images without the interference of the earth's atmosphere. It would also not be affected by the movement of the earth and it would not be limited to one position on the earth.**

2. What kinds of things can we learn from using optical telescopes? **What a star looks like, its color, brilliance, etc. Astronomers have observed that occasionally what appears to be only one star might actually be two stars.**

3. What kinds of things can we learn from radio telescopes? **The radio wave activity of a star or other object in space can be detected. Different substances emit different wavelengths of radio waves so the composition of a star can be determined. Also, using radio waves as radar allows us to get an idea of the density of planets.**

5. Overview of the Universe

What did we learn?

1. What is our solar system? **The group of heavenly bodies that includes our sun and the planets that revolve around it.**

2. Our solar system is part of which galaxy? **The Milky Way galaxy.**

3. How big is the universe? **No one knows for sure. Some people believe that is has no end.**

Taking it further

1. Why do you think our galaxy is called the Milky Way? **Because on clear nights the stars in the galaxy make a white milky band across the sky.**

2. Why do you need star charts that are different for different times of the year? **Because as the earth travels around the sun, it is in a slightly different position with respect to the stars each day.**

3. Why do you need star charts that are different for different times of the night? **Because as the earth rotates on its axis, a particular spot on the earth moves with respect to the stars.**

Challenge questions – Locating stars

1. Explain how a star map is similar to a map of the globe. **They both have an equator and prime longitude line. They both allow you to locate areas using the equivalent of latitude and longitude.**

2. What units are used to measure declination and ascension? **Declination—degrees north or south, ascension—hours and minutes.**

3. How does an astronomer define a constellation differently than most people? **To an astronomer, a constellation is an area in the sky; to most people, a constellation is a collection of stars that forms a picture of sorts.**

6. Stars

What did we learn?

1. What is the unit of distance used to measure how far away something is in space? **Light-year.**

2. How far is a light-year? **The distance light travels in one year—about 6 trillion miles.**

3. What does the color of a star tell us about that star? **Its approximate surface temperature; blue stars are much hotter than yellow or red stars.**

Taking it further

1. What causes stars to appear to move in the sky? **Most apparent motion is caused by the movement of the earth.**

2. How can we determine if a star's absolute distance from the earth is actually changing over time? **We must measure its light over a long period of time and see if it is changing.**

3. Why is brightness not a good indicator of the distance of a star from the earth? **Brightness is determined by the amount of light emitted and how far the star is from the earth. Brighter stars may be farther away but emitting more light, or they may be closer and emitting less light. You need to know how much light is being emitted, as well as the brightness, to determine the distance of the star from earth.**

Starlight worksheet

1. What happened to the light beam as the flashlight was moved farther from the wall? **The beam got wider but was not as intense; the closer one would appear brighter.**

2. How would two identical stars appear to someone on earth if one was much farther away? **The one farther away would appear smaller and dimmer than the closer one.**

3. **Answers will vary.**

4. Why could two stars with the same apparent brightness be different distances from the earth? **Because the way the stars appear to us is determined by the brightness of the star and the distance to the star; if one star was much brighter than the other but also farther away, the same amount of light could be hitting the earth from both stars. This would make them appear the same to us.**

7. Heavenly Bodies

What did we learn?

1. What is a cluster of stars? **A group of stars that appear to move together.**

2. What is a galaxy? **A group of millions (or billions) of stars that rotates around a central point.**

3. Explain the difference between a nova, a supernova, and a neutron star. **A nova is a star that is exploding and then returns to normal. A supernova is a star that experiences such a huge explosion that it may be destroyed. A neutron star is believed to be what is left of a supernova. It is extremely small and dense and emits radio waves.**

Taking it further

1. How can a star appear to become brighter and dimmer on a regular basis? **If two stars rotate around each other, they can line up so that they appear as one bright star. Later, one star can block the light of the other making it appear dimmer. Also, some stars expand and contract on a regular basis causing them to appear brighter and dimmer—these are called Cepheid variable stars.**

2. Why does starlight from millions of light-years away not prove that the earth is old? **There are several ideas using general relativity that explain how time may have passed more slowly on earth while billions of years were passing on the stars in the expanding universe.**

8. Asteroids

What did we learn?

1. What is an asteroid? **A relatively small rock in a regular orbit around the sun.**

2. Where are most asteroids in our solar system located? **In the asteroid belt between the orbits of Mars and Jupiter.**

3. What is another name for asteroids? **Minor planets.**

Taking it further

1. What is the chance that an asteroid will hit the earth? **Relatively small. As Christians we must trust God that all things, including asteroids, are in His control.**

Challenge – Trojan asteroids

Some of the names of the Trojan asteroids include: **Achilles, Hektor, Nestor, Agamemnon, Odysseus, Ajax, Diomedes, Antilochus, and Menelaus.**

9. Comets

What did we learn?

1. What is a comet? **A frozen core of rock and dust that orbits the sun in a regular orbit.**

2. Who was the first person to accurately predict the orbit of comets? **Edmond Halley.**

3. What are the two main parts of a comet? **Head, tail.**

Taking it further

1. Why does a comet's tail always point away from the sun? **The solar winds that cause the tail are always moving away from the sun.**

2. Why doesn't a comet have a tail when it is far from the sun? **There are no solar winds to push it, and it does not vaporize when it is far from the sun.**

3. When will Halley's Comet next appear? **1986+75 = 2061.**

Challenge questions – God created comets

1. "Lift up your eyes to the heavens, And look on the earth beneath. For the heavens will vanish away like smoke, The earth will grow old like a garment, And those who dwell in it will die in like manner; But My salvation will be forever, And My righteousness will not be abolished." —Isaiah 51:6
Comets become smaller every time they pass the sun. Thus they are wearing out just as the earth and the rest of the universe is wearing out.

2. Then God said, "Let there be lights in the firmament of the heavens to divide the day from the night; and let them be for signs and seasons, and for days and years." —Genesis 1:15
Comets make regular paths around the sun, thus they can be used for telling seasons, days, and years.

3. Thus says the Lord: "Do not learn the way of the Gentiles; Do not be dismayed at the signs of heaven, For the Gentiles are dismayed at them." —Jeremiah 10:2
Many cultures, especially ancient cultures, viewed unusual activity in the heavens as bad omens, so the appearance of a comet would have been considered a bad omen. But God says not to be dismayed by them. Because they have regular orbits, their appearances can be predicted and there is nothing to fear.

4. "In the beginning was the Word, and the Word was with God, and the Word was God. He was in the beginning with God. All things were made through Him, and without Him nothing was made that was made." —John 1:1–3
There is no evidence for a comet nursery; comets were created in the beginning by God.

10. Meteors

What did we learn?

1. What is the difference between a meteoroid, meteor, and meteorite? **Meteoroids are small pieces of rock and other debris floating in space—usually orbiting the sun. Meteors are meteoroids that get close enough to the earth to be pulled in by the earth's gravity. Meteorites are meteors that reach the surface of the earth.**

2. When is the best time to watch for meteors? **After midnight on any evening and especially around August 12 and November 17.**

Taking it further

1. Space dust (extremely small meteorites) is constantly falling on the earth. If this has been going on for billions of years, what would you expect to find on the earth and in the oceans? **You would expect to find many meteorites in the fossil layers. You would also expect to find many feet of space dust accumulating in the oceans.**

2. Have we discovered these things? **No. There have been very few confirmed meteorites found in the fossil layers, and a very small amount of space dust found in the oceans. Both of these facts indicate that the earth is relatively young.**

11. Overview of Our Solar System

What did we learn?

1. Name the eight planets in our solar system. **Mercury, Venus, Earth, Mars, Jupiter, Saturn, Uranus, and Neptune—Pluto is no longer considered a planet, but a plutoid.**

2. Name two dwarf planets. **Ceres, Pluto, and Eris were mentioned in this lesson.**

3. Which planets can support life? **Only earth.**

Taking it further

1. What are the major differences between the inner and outer planets? **Inner planets are closer to the sun, smaller, and are terrestrial (solid rock). Outer planets are larger and made from gas.**

2. Why are the gas planets called Jovian planets? **Jovian means Jupiter-like. Jupiter is a gas giant. The other planets that are also comprised of gas, like Jupiter, are thus called Jovian.**

12. Our Sun

What did we learn?

1. What are the main elements found in the sun? **95% of the sun is hydrogen and helium.**

2. What colors are found in sunlight? **All colors from violet to red.**

Taking it further

1. Why is the sun so important to us? **Its gravity holds everything in our solar system in place; it provides heat, light, and energy for life.**

2. How does energy get from the sun to the earth? **It travels in waves—light, heat, radio, and x-rays.**

Sun Measurement worksheet

1. What could account for the differences in your calculated value versus the known value? **The circle is small, so exact measurements are difficult to make. This causes error so your answer will differ from the expected value.**

2. How does the diameter of the sun compare with the diameter of the earth? **The diameter of the earth is approximately 7,927 miles. The diameter of the sun is about 109 times bigger.**

13. Structure of the Sun

What did we learn?

1. What are the two parts of the sun's atmosphere? **The chromosphere and the corona.**

2. What is a sunspot? **An area on the sun's surface that is cooler than surrounding areas.**

3. Are sunspots stationary? **No, they tend to move from east to west across the surface of the sun.**

4. What do scientists believe are the three parts of the sun's interior? **The core, radiative zone, and convective zone.**

Taking it further

1. What is the hottest part of the sun? **The core, which is believed to be nearly 25 million degrees Fahrenheit.**

2. What causes the aurora borealis or northern lights? **Particles emitted by a solar flare light up when they reach the earth's ionosphere.**

3. When do you think scientists study the sun's corona? **Accept reasonable answers. The following answer is from Lesson 14: The best time is during a solar eclipse. Scientists can see and study the corona while the rest of the sun is hidden by the moon.**

14. Solar Eclipse

What did we learn?

1. What is an eclipse? **When one heavenly body blocks the light from another heavenly body.**

2. What is the difference between a partial and a total eclipse? **A partial eclipse only covers part of the sun's disk, while a total eclipse covers it completely.**

3. How often do solar eclipses occur? **1 to 3 times each year.**

Taking it further

1. Why do you think plants and animals start preparing for nightfall during an eclipse? **Their instincts tell them that the sun is going down.**

2. Why can a total eclipse only be seen in a small area on the earth? **The shadow of the moon is only about 150 miles across.**

3. How can the moon block out the entire sun when the sun is 400 times bigger than the moon? **The moon is 400 times closer to the earth than the sun is, so from the earth they appear to be about the same size.**

15. Solar Energy

What did we learn?

1. What is solar energy? **Energy we get from the sun.**

2. What are the two ways that solar energy is used today? **To heat water and to generate electricity.**

Taking it further

1. Why is solar energy a good alternative to fossil fuels? **It is clean, readily available, and virtually unlimited.**

2. Why are the insides of solar collectors painted black? **Black absorbs the heat from the sun so black solar collectors are more efficient than other colors would be.**

3. What are some of the advantages of using solar cells in outer space? **Other fuel sources would be too heavy**

to launch into space, but solar panels are very light. The sun shines all the time in space and there is no atmosphere to block the sun's energy.**

Challenge questions – Solar energy

1. Is the new pattern bigger or smaller than the first pattern? **It should be bigger. The same amount of light is hitting the paper in both instances, but when the paper is at an angle, the light is more spread out, or dispersed.**

2. Based on what you just learned, where would be the best location for a solar energy power plant? **The light hits the earth most directly at the equator, so a solar power plant would work best near the equator in an area that gets relatively few clouds.**

Solar Energy worksheet

1. **Answers will vary.**

2. **Answers will vary.**

3. **Answers will vary.**

4. What color would you use to paint a solar collector? **Dark colors absorb more heat than light colors and dull surfaces absorb more heat than shiny ones. So solar collectors are painted with a dull black paint.**

16. Our Moon

What did we learn?

1. Why does the moon shine? **It reflects the light from the sun.**

2. What causes the dark spots on the surface of the moon? **They are plains that are covered with hardened basalt.**

Taking it further

1. Why does the size of our moon show God's provision for man? **It is much larger than most moons. This allows it to reflect a significant amount of light, lighting up the night.**

2. Why is gravity much less on the moon than on the earth? **The moon is much less massive than the earth, and gravity is a function of mass.**

3. Why doesn't the surface of the earth have as many craters as the surface of the moon? **Most meteors burn up in our atmosphere before they reach the earth's surface, but the moon does not have an atmosphere to protect it.**

17. Motion & Phases of the Moon

What did we learn?

1. What causes the phases of the moon? **The orbit of the moon around the earth causes it to be in a different position with respect to the sun each day.**

2. Why does the same side of the moon always face the earth? **The moon rotates on its axis at the same rate that it revolves around the earth.**

3. What causes a lunar eclipse? **The earth passes directly between the moon and the sun, blocking the light of the sun from the moon.**

4. From the perspective of space, how long does it take for the moon to complete its cycle around the earth? **27.3 days, or about a month.**

Taking it further

1. Why doesn't a lunar eclipse occur every month? **The moon's orbit is tilted 5 degrees from the earth's orbit so the sun, earth, and moon don't line up perfectly very often.**

2. What is the difference between a waxing crescent and a waning crescent? **The waxing crescent is lit up on the right side of the moon from the earth's perspective, and is getting larger; the waning crescent is lit up on the left side of the moon, and is getting smaller.**

Challenge questions – Observing the moon

1. When is the light side of the moon the same as the near side of the moon? **Full moon.**

2. When is the dark side of the moon the same as the near side of the moon? **New moon.**

Identifying Phases of the Moon worksheet

1. **New moon**
2. **Waxing crescent**
3. **First quarter**
4. **Waxing gibbous**
5. **Full moon**
6. **Waning gibbous**
7. **Last quarter**
8. **Waning crescent**

18. Origin of the Moon

What did we learn?

1. What are four secular theories for the origin of the moon? **Capture Theory, Fission Theory, Accretion, and Impact Theory.**

2. Which of these theories is most likely to be true? **None. They all have significant problems.**

3. What does the Bible say about the origin of the moon? **It says that God created the moon on Day 4 to light up the night.**

Taking it further

1. What are the main difficulties with the Capture Theory? **Scientists cannot explain what would cause the moon to leave its original orbit. The probability that the moon would approach the earth at exactly the right angle and speed to result in the moon orbiting the earth is extremely small.**

2. Why do you think scientists come up with unworkable ideas for the moon's origin? **Scientists try to find answers to important questions. They come up with ideas for possible solutions. These are called hypotheses. They then test their hypotheses to see if they are true or not. Sometimes a hypothesis is wrong and should be cast aside. Generally, there are two problems with hypotheses concerning origins: 1. We cannot adequately test them because we cannot recreate the conditions under which the event took place; and 2. Many scientists are unwilling to consider the option that God exists, much less that He created things; therefore, many scientists still cling to unworkable ideas rather than admit that something outside of natural causes exists.**

Challenge questions – Origin of the moon

- **Genesis 1:14–19 - God spoke the moon into existence on the fourth day of creation. Ps. 8:3–4 - The moon is the work of God's fingers; He set it in place. Ps. 33:6 - The heavens were made by God's word. Ps. 74:16 - God established the moon. Ps. 136:3–9 - God made the moon by His understanding (or wisdom). Jer. 31:35 - The Lord decreed the moon to shine.**

- **These verses clearly show that God created the moon out of nothing by speaking it into existence. They adequately explain the origin of the moon. The naturalistic explanations all have significant problems that cannot be explained by naturalistic means.**

19. Mercury

What did we learn?

1. How do Mercury's revolution around the sun and rotation on its axis compare to that of Earth? **Mercury travels quickly around the sun, but turns slowly on its axis compared to Earth.**

2. What is the surface of Mercury like? **Very hot or very cold, solid with lots of craters.**

Taking it further

1. How does a lack of atmosphere affect the conditions on Mercury? **It causes extreme temperature swings and allows meteorites to strike the surface.**

20. Venus

What did we learn?

1. Where is Venus's orbit with respect to the sun and the other planets? **It is second from the sun.**

2. What makes Venus so bright in the sky? **Its atmosphere reflects the light of the sun.**

3. What is a nickname for Venus? **The Morning Star or the Evening Star.**

4. How many moons does Venus have? **None.**

Taking it further

1. Even though Venus has an atmosphere, why can't life exist there? **The atmosphere is poisonous to people, plants, and animals. Also, it makes the planet too hot. The thick atmosphere also exerts too much pressure and would crush any living creatures.**

2. Why doesn't the earth's atmosphere keep our planet too hot? **It is not nearly as thick as the atmosphere on Venus and it is composed of different gases. There is some concern about the greenhouse effect increasing on the earth because of increased carbon dioxide in the air. Some scientists feel that this is a real threat, while others feel that it is not. Most evidence points to higher carbon dioxide levels in the past, which may have actually been beneficial and not harmful. More study is needed in this area.**

Greenhouse Effect worksheet

1. What did you observe about the temperature in the box when it was covered with plastic wrap? **The temperature goes up inside the box.**

2. Why did the temperature do this? **The plastic wrap traps some of the sun's rays.**

3. What do you think the temperature would be inside the box if you left it in the sun for several hours? **The temperature will continue to rise for some time and then level off**.

21. Earth

What did we learn?

1. What are some features of our planet that make it uniquely able to support life? **Just the right distance from the sun, axis is tilted just right to make most of the earth able to grow food, large amount of water, right atmosphere and weather patterns.**

2. What name is given to the period of time it takes for Earth's revolution around the sun? **Year.**

3. What name is given to the length of Earth's rotation on its axis? **Day.**

4. On average, how far is Earth from the sun? **About 93 million miles or 150 million km.**

Taking it further

1. What are some possible reasons why large amounts of water are found on Earth but not on other planets? **Some planets are too hot and water evaporates away; some planets do not have enough gravity to hold an atmosphere so water also evaporates away; other planets do not have the right elements readily available; but most importantly, God created this planet uniquely for us.**

2. Why is it important that Earth is a terrestrial planet? **This means Earth has a solid surface for us to live on.**

22. Mars

What did we learn?

1. Why is Mars called a superior planet? **It has an orbit that is larger than Earth's orbit.**

2. Why is Mars called the red planet? **Its soil has a red color due to a high amount of iron oxide—rust.**

3. How many moons does Mars have? **2—Phobos and Deimos.**

Taking it further

1. What causes the dust storms on Mars? **Heat from the sun causes winds that pick up dust.**

2. Why doesn't the wind on Earth cause giant dust storms like the wind on Mars? **Although heat from the sun does cause wind, most of Earth is covered with water. Also, the land is mostly covered with vegetation that holds down the soil, so giant dust storms are unlikely. Small dust and sand storms do happen on Earth.**

3. How would your weight on Mars compare to your weight on Mercury? **They would be about the same because the gravity is about the same on both planets.**

Experimenting with polar ice caps

1. What was the "smoke" coming off of the dry ice? **Carbon dioxide gas.**

2. Why did the candle flame go out? **The carbon dioxide in the cup was heavier than air and pushed the oxygen away from the candle so the flame went out.**

3. Why did the water in the cup "boil"? **As the dry ice melted it quickly turned to gas, which bubbled to the surface of the water.**

23. Jupiter

What did we learn?

1. What are some major differences between Jupiter and the inner planets? **The inner planets are solid and relatively small. Jupiter is very large and made of gas.**

2. What is the Great Red Spot? **It is believed to be a giant wind storm that has lasted hundreds of years.**

Taking it further

1. Why does Jupiter bulge more in the middle than Earth does? **Jupiter spins faster on its axis than Earth does, causing more outward or centrifugal force.**

2. Why can't life exist on Jupiter? **The temperatures are too cold, the surface is not solid, there is no air to breathe.**

3. Why are space probes necessary for exploring other planets? **Probes can go where people can't. They can see things up close that we cannot see from Earth. For example, *Voyager* discovered a ring around Jupiter. Also, probes can go into environments that are difficult for humans to enter such as Venus's carbon dioxide**

and sulfuric acid atmosphere. **Probes can do tests in far away places like the soil tests done on Mars by the *Spirit* and *Opportunity* rovers.**

24. Saturn

What did we learn?

1. Who first saw Saturn's rings? **Galileo; however he did not recognize them as rings. Christian Huygens first identified the rings.**

2. What are Saturn's rings made of? **Pieces of ice, dust, and rock.**

3. What makes Titan unique among moons? **It is the only moon with an atmosphere.**

Taking it further

1. Why did astronomers believe that Saturn had only a few rings before the *Voyager* space probe explored Saturn? **That was all that could be observed from Earth using telescopes.**

2. Both Titan and Earth have a mostly nitrogen atmosphere. What important differences exist between these two worlds that make Earth able to support life but Titan unable to? **Titan is too far away from the sun, and thus is too cold to support life. Also, Titan's atmosphere has methane and no oxygen. Earth has just the right amount of oxygen to support life.**

25. Uranus

What did we learn?

1. What makes Uranus unusual compared to the other planets? **It rotates on its side.**

2. How have rings been discovered around Uranus? **By telescopes and space probes.**

Taking it further

1. How can we learn more about Uranus? **Send out more probes; build better telescopes.**

2. Why is Uranus such a cold planet? **It is too far from the sun for the sun to heat it very much.**

26. Neptune

What did we learn?

1. What similarities are there between Uranus and Neptune? **They are both gas planets and have**

rings and moons. They both have methane in their atmospheres that make them appear blue. They were both discovered in the last 250 years.

2. What are two possible explanations for the Great Dark Spot? **Some scientists believe it was a giant windstorm in Neptune's atmosphere, others believe it may have been a hole in the clouds surrounding the planet.**

Taking it further

1. Explain how Neptune was discovered. **Observations of Uranus's orbit indicated that there must be a planet whose gravity was affecting Uranus. Astronomers/ mathematicians calculated where the unknown planet had to be and another astronomer found it there.**

2. What affects the color of a planet? **Many things can affect what color a planet appears to be. Mars is red because of the rust (iron oxide) in its soil; Earth appears blue because of the water on the surface and its atmosphere; Uranus and Neptune appear blue because of the methane in their atmospheres.**

Challenge questions – Centripetal force

1. Were you able to spin the washer as slowly after your shortened the string? **No.**

2. How does the pressure between your hand and the string compare when the string is short and when the string is long? **The pressure is greater when the string is short.**

27. Pluto & Eris

What did we learn?

1. What discovery was originally considered to be the ninth planet? **Pluto.**

2. How does the gravity on Pluto compare to the gravity on Earth? **There is practically no gravity on Pluto. It is 0.08 times the gravity on Earth.**

3. Is Pluto always farther away from the sun than Neptune? **No, it is closer to the sun than Neptune for 20 out of every 250 years.**

4. What is unique about how Charon orbits Pluto? **They are in a synchronous orbit—the same sides of the planet and moon always face each other.**

Taking it further

1. Why did it take so long to discover Pluto? **It's a small planet and very far away. It was much dimmer than expected.**

2. Why is Pluto no longer considered to be a planet? **It is too small; it does not meet the definition for a planet adopted by the International Astronomical Union.**

3. What alternate classification was given to Pluto in 2006? **It was called a dwarf planet.**

28. NASA

What did we learn?

1. What is NASA? **The National Aeronautics and Space Administration, a science organization for studying the universe.**

2. When was NASA formed? **1958.**

3. What was one of NASA's first tasks? **To put a man on the moon.**

4. List at least three different types of projects that a person at NASA could work on. **Possible answers include: Design and develop better tools and technologies, plan projects to put humans and robots into space, collect and analyze data, plan and oversee missions.**

Taking it further

1. How does NASA help people who are not interested in space exploration? **By developing technology that is applicable in other areas.**

2. How might an evolutionary worldview affect NASA's work? **Many of NASA's projects are dedicated to finding life on Mars or other planets/moons; others are designed to prove the big bang. If NASA had a biblical worldview, their missions could be discovering the wonders of the universe that glorify God.**

Challenge questions – NACA

1. What was NACA? **National Advisory Committee for Aeronautics.**

2. What was its original purpose? **To supervise and direct the scientific study of the problems of flight, with a view to their practical solution.**

3. What were some of the major contributions to aeronautics that were made by NACA? **Supersonic**

and hypersonic flight technology, safety designs, improved engines, airfoils, and wings.

29. Space Exploration

What did we learn?

1. Who were the first people to talk about going into space? **The science fiction writers of the 19th century.**

2. Who is considered the father of modern rocketry? **Robert H. Goddard.**

3. What major event sparked interest in the development of the rocket for space travel? **The extensive use of rockets during World War II.**

4. Who was one of the primary developers of rockets in the United States after World War II? **The German scientist, Wernher von Braun.**

5. What was the first man-made object to orbit the earth? **Sputnik — a satellite launched by the Soviet Union.**

6. Who was the first man in space? **Yuri Gagarin.**

7. Who was the first American in space? **Alan Shepherd.**

8. Who was the first American to orbit the earth? **John Glenn.**

9. Who was the first man to walk on the moon? **Neil Armstrong.**

Taking it further

1. Why are satellites an important part of space exploration? **Satellites have many purposes including collecting scientific and military data, communications, and navigation.**

2. Why are space probes an important part of space exploration? **Probes can go to places that are too far away for humans to travel and places that are too dangerous for humans. The atmosphere on Venus crushed several of the early probes that were sent there. Losing a probe is a risk worth taking, but risking human life is not. Most of the information we have about the other planets has come from space probes.**

30. Apollo Program

What did we learn?

1. What was the name of the NASA program whose goal was to put a man on the moon? **Apollo.**

2. What are the three modules in the Apollo spacecraft? **The command module, the service module, and the lunar module.**

3. What were the two parts of the lunar module designed to do? **The descent stage allowed astronauts to land on the moon. The ascent stage lifted them from the moon back to the command module in lunar orbit.**

4. What was the name of the three-stage rocket used with the Apollo spacecraft? **Saturn V.**

Taking it further

1. What is the advantage of a multi-stage rocket engine? **The first engine must lift all of the weight of the combined system, but the second engine only needs to lift the weight of the system after the first stage is gone, so it does not need to be as big. The third stage is only needed to break the modules out of earth's orbit, so it can be relatively small.**

31. The Space Shuttle

What did we learn?

1. What was the main advantage of the space shuttle vehicle over all previous manned space vehicles? **The shuttle was reusable, thus it was much less expensive to operate.**

2. What were the main purposes of the shuttle program? **Scientific experiments, launching of space satellites, and ferrying astronauts and supplies to the space station.**

3. What were the two main parts of the orbiter and what were their purposes? **The crew cabin contained the flight deck and living areas. The payload bay provided room for satellites and experiments. It also provided an area where repair work could be done.**

Taking it further

1. Why was the space shuttle called an orbiter? **It was designed to orbit the earth for experimental purposes. It was not designed for outer space flight.**

2. Why was the orbiter shaped like an airplane? **The shape of a space vehicle is relatively unimportant in space because there is no gravity and no atmosphere. However, the shuttle had to land safely on earth. So it was designed with aerodynamics similar to an airplane, so it could land like a plane in the earth's atmosphere.**

3. Why did the orbiter have to be carried back to Florida if it landed in California? **The shuttle did not have any jet engines or any way to propel itself through the atmosphere. It only had booster engines that allowed it to move in space. So, although it may have resembled an airplane, it couldn't fly like one.**

Space Shuttle worksheet
See drawing in student manual on page 272.

32. International Space Station

What did we learn?

1. What is the International Space Station? **A permanent orbiting laboratory in space.**

2. Why do countries feel there is a need for a space station? **To study long-term effects of micro-gravity for scientific purposes and to develop new technologies to benefit all of humanity.**

Taking it further

1. What shape would you expect a flame to be on the space station? **A candle flame is somewhat teardrop shaped on earth. However, in space it is circular because the oxygen molecules are equally available from all directions and are not being pulled down by gravity.**

33. Astronauts

What did we learn?

1. What are some ways that astronauts train for their missions? **They learn about the vehicles they will be using and the experiments they will be performing.**

They practice in their spacesuits underwater. They ride in the "Vomit Comet."

2. What conditions in space require astronauts to need spacesuits? **There is no atmosphere in space so there is no pressure, no oxygen, and no protection from the hot and cold extremes in space. Also, there is more radiation in space so extra protection is needed.**

Taking it further

1. What are some things you can do if you want to become an astronaut? **Study math and science, keep physically fit, and work hard.**

2. What would you like to do if you were involved in the space program? **Answers will vary.**

34. Solar System Model: Final Project

What did we learn?

1. What holds all of the planets in orbit around the sun? **The force of gravity.**

2. What other items are in our solar system that are not included in your model? **Asteroids, comets, meteoroids, Pluto and other dwarf planets.**

Taking it further

1. Why do the planets orbit the sun and not the earth? **The sun is the most massive object in the solar system. It therefore has the strongest gravitational pull so smaller items, such as planets, will orbit it.**

35. Conclusion

What did we learn?

1. What is the best thing you learned about our universe? **Answers will vary.**

Our Planet Earth ⟶ **Worksheet** Answer Keys

1. Introduction to Earth Science

What did we learn?

1. What are the four main studies of earth science? **Space/astronomy, atmosphere/meteorology, lithosphere/geology, and water/hydrology.**

2. What is one question mentioned in this lesson that science cannot answer about the earth? **Where it came from originally. There are many other questions beyond science as well.**

3. Why can we rely on God's Word to tell us where the earth came from? **The Bible is the Word of God and God does not lie. The evidence around us confirms what the Bible says.**

Taking it further

1. How does the first law of thermodynamics confirm the Genesis account of creation? **Since energy cannot be created by natural means, then a supernatural event must have occurred to make the energy and matter in the universe. The Bible says God spoke it into existence.**

2. How does the second law of thermodynamics confirm the Genesis account of creation? **If the whole universe is slowing down and losing energy, there must have been a time when everything was started—when the energy was put into the whole system. Together with the first law, this shows that a supernatural event, such as the creation described in the Bible, must have happened in the past.**

3. Read Psalm 139:8–10. What do these verses say about where we can find God? **God is present everywhere, even in space or at the bottom of the ocean; wherever we go, God is with us.**

2. Introduction to Geology

What did we learn?

1. What is geology? **The study of the earth and the processes that affect it.**

2. What are some of the evidences that God designed the earth uniquely to support life? **The abundance of water and its properties, just the right amount of oxygen in the atmosphere, the distance of the earth from the sun, the tilt of the earth.**

Taking it further

1. List some ways that geology affects your life on a regular basis. **Minerals and metals are in nearly every object around you. You use gas in your car. Your house must be built on a firm foundation.**

2. What area of geology interests you the most? **Go to the library and learn more about it.**

Challenge – Elements
You are likely to find sodium, potassium, phosphorus, magnesium, zinc, copper, iron, and calcium.

Geology Scavenger Hunt

1. Milk

2. Toothpaste

3. Salt

4. Cereal

5. Pencils

6. Chalk

7. Matches

8. Baby powder

9. Rechargable batteries

10. Drywall

11. Computer chips

12. Pennies

13. Electrical wiring

14. Thermometer

15. Paper clip or staple

3. The Earth's History

What did we learn?

1. What are the two most popular views for how the earth became what it is today? **Creation/biblical and evolution/uniformitarian.**

2. According to the Bible, what are the three major events that affected the way the earth looks today? **Creation, the Fall of man, the Flood.**

3. Should a good scientist disregard evidence that contradicts his/her ideas? **No, he/she should examine the evidence and try to understand why it does not agree. Sometimes the answer cannot be found now, but may be obvious later, when other discoveries are made.**

4. Have scientists proven that evolution is true? **No! Evolution is a model of origins that cannot be proven, and actually contradicts what we observe. A historical event, such as the origin of the world, cannot be recreated or tested, so it cannot be proven. We must trust the account of the One who was there—God.**

5. Have scientists proven that biblical creation is true? **No. Creation and evolution both deal with historical events—origins science. Neither can be proven by science. But, when the evidence is examined, it contradicts the evolutionary view and confirms the Bible's account.**

Taking it further

1. How might scientists explain the discovery of fossilized seashells in the middle of a desert? **An ocean must have covered the desert at one time. The Bible says the whole world was covered with water during the Flood. Evolutionists say the climate was very different in the past, causing the oceans to cover more of the world.**

2. Explain how a fossilized tree could be found upright through several layers of rock. **The tree had to have been covered with the various layers before it had a chance to decay. This must have occurred relatively quickly, over a few years time, not over millions of years. In fact, we see an example where hundreds of trees are settling upright into sediment at the bottom of Spirit Lake following the 1980 eruption of Mount St. Helens.**

4. The Genesis Flood

What did we learn?

1. What are some things geologists observe that point to a worldwide flood? **Large amounts of sedimentary rock, abundant fossils, most fossils are aquatic.**

2. What major geological events may have been associated with the Flood of Noah's day? **Major volcanic activity, separation of the landmasses, the Ice Age, formation of mountain ranges.**

Taking it further

1. How would a huge flood change the way the earth looks? **Rushing water would cause massive erosion, wearing away rock. This would cause valleys to form and would move rock and soil from one place to another. It would also bury massive amounts of plants and animals under thick layers of mud resulting in abundant fossils, as well as coal and oil deposits.**

2. Why did God send a huge flood? **To punish man for his wickedness.**

Challenge – Did the Flood Really Happen? worksheet

1. _**Yes**_ Water would wash away rocks, soil, and buildings.

2. _**Yes**_ Millions of animals and people would die.

3. _**Yes**_ The water would move rocks and soil from one place to another.

4. _**Yes**_ Buildings would be destroyed.

5. _**No**_ Land would be unchanged.

6. _**Yes**_ A large boat would float on the water.

7. _**Yes**_ Land animals would be covered with mud and sand.

8. _**Yes**_ Debris would settle out of the water.

9. _**No**_ Plants would not be uprooted or killed.

10. _**Yes**_ New paths would be formed for water to flow through.

With this in mind, list at least three things that you would expect to find hundreds or even thousands of years later when you dig into the earth.

1. **Millions of fossils—mostly of sea creatures found all over the world.**

2. **Fossils of sea creatures on the tops of high mountains.**

3. **Fossils of sea creatures in the middle of deserts.**

4. **Oil and coal that were formed from dead plants and sea creatures that were buried under tons of rock.**

5. **Layers of sedimentary rock.**

6. **Some rock layers are curved or folded as if they were all soft at the same time.**

7. **Deep canyons were carved.**

These are just a few evidences that support the idea of a worldwide flood.

5. The Great Ice Age

What did we learn?

1. What two conditions are necessary for an ice age? **Wetter winters and cooler summers.**

2. How did the Genesis Flood set up conditions for the Ice Age? **Warm oceans allowed for lots of evaporation and therefore lots of snow. Volcanic ash blocked much of the sunlight, causing much cooler summers.**

3. How do evolutionists explain the needed conditions for multiple ice ages? **They cannot adequately explain what causes the additional moisture or the cooler temperatures.**

Taking it further

1. Do you think there are new glaciers still forming today? **Accept reasonable answers. The following answer is from Lesson 6: We see some new glaciers forming and some old glaciers growing bigger for a few years, but not on the large scale they did during the Ice Age.**

Ice Age Crossword Puzzle

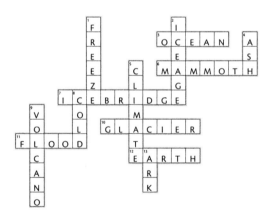

6. Glaciers

What did we learn?

1. What is a glacier? **A formation of ice that does not completely melt from year to year.**

2. How does a glacier form? **The snow accumulates each year because it does not completely melt during the summer. The weight of the snow compacts the snow below it, eventually turning it to ice.**

3. What are the three types of glaciers? **Valley—forms in a valley, Piedmont—spreads out from two or more valleys, Continental—forms in a relatively flat area and spreads out in all directions.**

4. What is calving? **When glaciers reach water and pieces break off into the water.**

Taking it further

1. Why do glaciers exist mostly at the poles and on high mountain tops? **That is where it stays cold enough in the summers to keep the snow and ice from completely melting.**

2. Why is it cold enough to prevent glaciers from melting at the North Pole, when there is 20–24 hours of sunlight during the summer? **Even though there are many hours of sunlight, the light hits the earth at a steep angle, so most of the heat is reflected.**

7. Movement of Glaciers

What did we learn?

1. What is the shape of a valley carved by glaciers? **U-shaped.**

2. How do glaciers pick up rocks and other debris? **They melt, and the water flows around the rocks; then the water refreezes and the rocks become part of the glacier.**

3. What is the name of the line of rocks that marks the farthest advance of the glacier? **Terminal moraine.**

Taking it further

1. How might a scientist tell how far a glacier moved a rock or boulder? **One way is to test what kind of rock the boulder is made of. Often, it is a different type than the rocks around it. Then, the scientist must trace the path of the glacier backward to where that type of rock is found.**

2. Why do glaciers often have deep cracks and crevices? **The lower layers of ice move smoothly while the upper layers, which are less compressed, are more brittle and break rather than move with the glacier.**

Making a mini-glacier

1. How did the movement of the ice affect the surface of the hill? **Answers will vary.**

2. Can you see striations — lines made in the dirt by the sand and pebbles in the ice? **Answers will vary.**

3. Is there a line of dirt and rocks at the front edge of the glacier? **Answers will vary.**

4. What did you see after the ice melted? Is there an area of pebbles that moved with the glacier? **Answers will vary.**

8. Design of the Earth

What did we learn?

1. What do most scientists believe to be the three main parts of the earth? **The core, the mantle, and the crust.**

2. Which is the thickest part of the earth? **The mantle.**

3. Which is the thinnest part of the earth? **The crust.**

4. Where is the crust the thickest? **Under the mountains.**

Taking it further

1. Why do scientists believe the mantle is hotter and denser than the crust? **Earthquake or seismic waves travel more quickly through the mantle than through the crust.**

2. For what other things, besides the interior of the earth, do scientists have to develop models without actually seeing what they are describing? **Very small things like atoms, very large things like the universe, things they are designing like airplanes or space ships.**

9. Rocks

What did we learn?

1. What are rocks made from? **One or more minerals or organic materials.**

2. What are the three categories of rocks? **Igneous, sedimentary, and metamorphic.**

3. How is igneous rock formed? **Igneous rock forms when melted rock, called magma, cools.**

4. How is sedimentary rock formed? **Sedimentary rock forms when layers of sediment are pressed and cemented together in some way.**

5. How is metamorphic rock formed? **Metamorphic rock is formed when either igneous or sedimentary rock is exposed to high pressure and high temperature for an extended period of time. The rock's atomic structure is changed and it becomes a different type of rock.**

Taking it further

1. Why are rocks important? **They affect nearly every area of our lives.**

2. Where is a good place to look for rocks? **You can find rocks nearly everywhere. It depends on what specific kinds of rocks you are looking for. You will more easily find rocks in areas with little or no soil.**

3. Why is it better to store your rock samples in a box with dividers than in a bag? **Some rocks are harder than others. In a bag, the samples will hit against each other and may scratch or break each other.**

The Rock Cycle worksheet

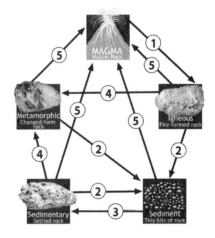

10. Igneous Rocks

What did we learn?

1. What is the difference between magma and lava? **Magma is inside the earth's crust and lava is on top of the earth's crust.**

2. How are extrusive rocks formed? **When magma flows to an area where it cools quickly, extrusive rocks are formed. This happens when lava flows to the surface of the earth's crust.**

3. How are intrusive rocks formed? **When magma flows to an area inside the crust that is cool enough for it to solidify, but at a slow rate, it forms intrusive rocks.**

Taking it further

1. Which kind of igneous rocks have the largest crystals? **The ones that were formed slowly—intrusive rocks.**

2. Why is granite commonly used in buildings and monuments? **It is hard and strong, and can be polished.**

3. Do all rocks sink in water? **No, pumice often floats.**

4. Why not? **Some rocks have air holes in them making them less dense than water, so they float.**

5. Where are you likely to find pumice? **Near a previously active volcano.**

11. Sedimentary Rocks

What did we learn?

1. How are sedimentary rocks formed? **When fragments of rocks and other debris settle out of water they form strata or layers. These layers are pressed together and glued with natural cement to form fragmental sedimentary rock. Chemical rock forms as chemicals precipitate from the water and harden into rock.**

2. Were all sedimentary rocks formed during the Flood? **No, but much of the sedimentary rock was probably formed then. New sedimentary rock is still being formed today, especially in caves and other wet areas.**

Taking it further

1. Why are fossils found in sedimentary rocks? **Fossils form when plants or animals are covered over with mud or other sediment shortly after dying. Sea creatures were covered over with layers of sediment during the Flood and these layers formed into much of the sedimentary rock we find today. Thus, most of the fossils are found in these rocks.**

2. Sediment is simply any small piece of something that settles out of a liquid. What sediment might you find around your house or in nature? **Coffee grounds, tea leaves, and orange juice pulp are a few sediments you might find around your house. Silt is a common sediment found in lakes and ponds. Glaciers melt and leave behind pebbles, rocks, and even boulders as sediment.**

12. Fossils

What did we learn?

1. How does an animal become a fossil? **If it is covered by mud, wet sand, or other similar substance shortly after it dies, instead of decaying, the hard structures can slowly be replaced by minerals.**

2. What are the two different types of fossils? **Cast fossils—imprints; Mold fossils—rock structures in the shape of the original structure.**

3. What types of creatures are most fossils? **95% of all fossils are sea invertebrates such as clams and other shellfish.**

Taking it further

1. How many true transitional fossils, ones showing one creature evolving into another, have been found? **None!**

2. What does this indicate about the theory that land animals evolved from sea creatures? **It shows that there is no physical evidence to support that theory.**

3. What are some things we can learn from fossils? **What kinds of plants and animals existed in the past, how those plants and animals were shaped compared to species that exist today, and what plants and animals are now extinct.**

4. What kinds of things cannot be learned from fossils? **Usually soft structures such as noses, hair, etc. are not preserved, so it is hard to tell exactly what a creature looked like. You can't tell its color either. Also, if only one or two bones are found, it is very difficult to know with certainty what that creature looked like. Some characteristics can be implied from fossil evidence but cannot be proven. For example, many scientists believe that at least some of the dinosaurs were warm-blooded because the distance between fossilized footprints indicates they must have been able to move quickly—an ability usually limited to warm-blooded creatures. However, this characteristic cannot be proven from the fossil evidence alone.**

13. Fossil Fuels

What did we learn?

1. What is the definition of a fossil fuel? **Fuel that was formed from dead plants or animals that were changed by heat and pressure over time.**

2. What three forms of fossil fuels do we commonly use? **Coal, oil/petroleum, and natural gas.**

Taking it further

1. What evidence supports rapid and recent coal formation instead of slow formation millions of years ago? **Carbon-14 dating, in spite of its limitations, supports recent formation. Boulders and delicate fossils in coal beds also show a young age.**

2. Why is finding natural gas when drilling into the ground a good indicator that oil is nearby? **Natural gas is believed to be a by-product of oil formation and is often found in the rocks surrounding an oil field.**

3. Why is the existence of natural gas an indication that oil was formed only a few thousand years ago? **Natural gas is a by-product of oil production. If the oil was formed millions of years ago, the gas would have escaped through the rocks by now.**

Challenge – What Would You Expect? worksheet

Lowest level	Upper level	Not found
Flies	Pine needles	Palm trees
Fish	Flies	Coconuts
Algae	Deer	Sea shells
Crawdads	Scrub oak	Parrots
Possibly wild flowers and pine needles	Wild flowers	Possibly crows
	Ground squirrel	
	Snakes	
	Rabbits	
	Possibly crows	

Accept reasonable answers.

1. Briefly explain why you put the items were you did. **Answers will vary.**

14. Metamorphic Rocks

What did we learn?

1. What are the three ingredients needed to change igneous or sedimentary rock into metamorphic rock? **Heat, pressure, and time.**

2. Why is marble often swirled instead of pure white? **There are often impurities in the limestone deposits that are a different color from the limestone.**

Taking it further

1. Why is metamorphic rock often used for sculptures and monuments? **It is usually very hard and durable. Nonfoliated rock has no crystal structure, so smoother edges are possible.**

2. Why is metamorphic rock hard and durable? **The heat and pressure rearrange the crystal structure to form very strong bonds.**

Morphing Ice worksheet

Heat only: the rock melts and becomes magma; Pressure only: the rock breaks into smaller pieces; Time only: nothing happens to the rock—it remains the same. Heat, pressure, and time: the rock is changed into metamorphic rock as the molecular structure of the rock changes.

Challenge — Metamorphic Match worksheet

_C_ Granite
_A_ Shale
_D_ Sandstone
_G_ Limestone
_B_ Mica
_F_ Basalt
_E_ Dolerite

15. Minerals

What did we learn?

1. What five requirements must a substance meet in order to be classified as a mineral? **Naturally occurring, inorganic, constant chemical proportions, regular structure and solid.**

2. What is a native mineral? **A mineral that has only one type of atom—a pure element.**

3. What is a compound? **A substance with two or more elements in fixed proportions.**

Taking it further

1. Are there any minerals that are mixtures? **No, mixtures do not have fixed proportions.**

2. What is the difference between a rock and a mineral? **Most minerals are compounds and most rocks are mixtures. Also, rocks can have organic compounds and minerals do not.**

3. Is coal a mineral? **No, it is an organic compound. It is a rock.**

4. Are all minerals considered rocks? **In their naturally occurring state, minerals are considered rocks.**

5. Are all rocks considered minerals? **No, most rocks are made of more than one kind of mineral.**

6. Where are you likely to find minerals? **Just about everywhere, such as in your body, your food, toothpaste, coins, cars, radios, TVs, etc.**

Mineral Scavenger Hunt worksheet

1. Water: **Is not a solid.**

2. Steel: **Is man-made.**

3. Coal: **Is organic (made from plants).**

4. Cookies: **Are mixtures made from varying amounts of minerals.**

5. Glass: **Does not have a crystalline structure.**

- **Minerals around my house include: Calcium in your milk, iron in nails, talc in powder, zinc in your breakfast cereal, fluoride in your toothpaste, etc.**

16. Identifying Minerals

What did we learn?

1. What are some common tests used to identify minerals? **Color, streak, luster, crystal shape, hardness, cleavage.**

2. Why is color alone not a sufficient test? **Many minerals have the same color. Also, the outside of a sample may change color when exposed to air or water.**

Taking it further

1. Is crystal size a good test for identifying a mineral? Why or why not? **No, the size of the crystals is dependent on the temperature at which the sample formed, but is not as dependent on the type of material. Crystal shape is a much better test.**

2. What is the difference between cleavage and fracture? **Cleavage indicates that a sample breaks smoothly in one or more directions—showing that the crystal structure is lined up in that direction. Fracture indicates that a sample breaks in smooth curves but not in straight lines.**

3. Why do some tests need to be done in a laboratory? **Some tests are too dangerous to do at home and others require special equipment.**

4. How can you tell a sample of sugar from a sample of salt? **You could taste the samples to determine which is sugar and which is salt if you are certain they are table salt and sugar. However, you should never taste an unknown sample. A better way would be to use a magnifying glass and observe the shape of the crystals. Salt crystals are usually perfect cubes and sugar crystals are longer and rectangular.**

Challenge – Is it a Rock or a Mineral? worksheet

Item	Element, compound, or mixture?	What are its main components?	Rock or mineral?
Gold	Element	Gold	Mineral
Granite	Mixture	Quartz, feldspar, and mica	Rock
Feldspar	Compound	Aluminum and silicon	Mineral
Quartz	Compound	Silicon and oxygen	Mineral
Limestone	Mixture	Calcium carbonate and other materials	Rock
Copper	Element	Copper	Mineral
Diamond	Element	Carbon	Mineral
Obsidian	Mixture	Glass containing silica, and aluminum	Rock
Gypsum	Compound	Calcium, sulfur, and oxygen	Mineral
Shale	Mixture	Clay and mud	Rock

17. Valuable Minerals

What did we learn?

1. What are some valuable minerals? **Gold, silver, copper, and diamonds.**

2. What is a native mineral? **A mineral made from just one kind of element.**

3. What are some important uses for gold? **Jewelry, electronics, money.**

4. What are some important uses for silver? **Jewelry, flatware, electronics, film processing.**

Taking it further

1. Why is diamond considered an exception among minerals? **Minerals are not supposed to contain carbon—they are inorganic. However, diamond is pure crystallized carbon.**

2. Diamonds and coal are both made from carbon. What makes them different? **Coal is a relatively soft black rock made from compressed plant material. Diamonds are carbon atoms that have crystallized due to extreme heat and pressure. Most geologists classify coal as a sedimentary rock and diamond as a metamorphic rock, although some geologists classify coal as a metamorphic rock as well.**

18. Natural & Artificial Gems

What did we learn?

1. What is a gem? **A mineral that is valued by people because of its beauty. Usually gems are brightly colored and have perfect cleavage that allows light to reflect through them.**

2. How is a gem different from a native mineral? **Native minerals have only one element. Diamonds are gems that are also native minerals. However, most gems are comprised of more than one element.**

3. How are artificial rubies made? **By melting the elements that make natural rubies, then allowing the materials to slowly cool and crystallize.**

Taking it further

1. What can you guess about the temperatures at which synthetic rubies are formed? **They are formed at high temperatures.**

2. Why would rubies be formed at high temperatures? **Recall from Lesson 10 that crystals grow larger when cooled more slowly, so rubies would be cooled at high temperatures to form larger crystals.**

3. What are some disadvantages of synthetic gems? **They are not as durable; they are not as valuable; they sometimes look different than naturally occurring gems.**

4. Why are natural gems worth more money than artificial gems? **Artificial gems are not as durable. Also, price is partially determined by availability. Natural gems are more scarce than artificial gems and are thus more expensive.**

19. Plate Tectonics

What did we learn?

1. What is plate tectonics? **The theory that the crust is made up of several large floating plates.**

2. How many plates do scientists think there are? **13 plates: 6 major, 7 minor.**

Taking it further

1. What are some things that are believed to have happened in the past because of the movement of the tectonic plates? **Continents separated by sea-floor spreading, mountains and ocean basins were formed, volcanic activity.**

2. What are some things that happen today because of the movement of the tectonic plates? **Earthquakes, volcanic activity, forming of faults and rifts.**

20. Mountains

What did we learn?

1. What is a mountain? **A rise in land with steep sides going up to a summit.**

2. What is a mountain range? **A series of mountain peaks in a given area.**

3. What is the difference between actual height and elevation of a mountain? **Actual height is the difference between the base and summit of a mountain. Elevation is the height of the summit above sea level.**

Taking it further

1. Where are the mountains with the highest elevations located? **In the Himalayan Mountain system in the area between India and China.**

2. Is a 700-foot rise a mountain or a hill? **It depends on your perspective. In areas with 5,000 foot mountains, a 700-foot rise will probably be called a hill, but in a relatively flat area it may be called a mountain.**

Famous Mountains worksheet

1. _C_ Mountains of Ararat

2. _E_ Mount Sinai

3. _G_ Mount Moriah

4. _D_ Mount Carmel

5. _F_ Mount of Olives

6. _A_ Mount of Transfiguration

7. _B_ Mount Horeb (The Mountain of God)

21. Types of Mountains

What did we learn?

1. How are depositional mountains formed? **Debris such as ash, lava, sand, etc. is deposited over time, eventually forming a mountain.**

2. How are erosional mountains formed? **Large amounts of material are eroded away, such as by a flood, leaving behind mountains and valleys.**

3. How are fold and fault mountains formed? **Tectonic plates push against each other and the constant force causes rocks in the middle to fold or slip and push up to form mountains.**

Taking it further

Identify each mountain as either depositional, erosional, or fold:

1. Mount St. Helens: **This is a volcano—depositional.**

2. Bryce Canyon: **Area with many flat-topped sandstone mountains—erosional.**

3. Sand Dunes National Monument: **Sand deposited by water and wind—depositional.**

4. Rocky Mountains: **Large mountain range—fold.**

5. Grand Canyon: **Believed to be carved by a flood—erosional.**

6. Mount Everest: **Highest mountain on earth—fold.**

22. Earthquakes

What did we learn?

1. What is believed to be the cause of earthquakes? **Tectonic plates move against each other causing stress or strain on the rocks. When the stress becomes too great, the rocks move quickly, resulting in an earthquake.**

2. What is an aftershock? **A smaller quake that occurs after a major earthquake.**

3. What name is given to the area on the earth's surface above where an earthquake originates? **Epicenter.**

4. What is a fault? **A crack in the earth's crust resulting from an earthquake.**

Taking it further

1. How does the type of material affect the speed of the earthquake waves? **Earthquake waves move more quickly through rock and other dense materials. The waves slow down when traveling through sand, mud and liquid rock or magma.**

2. How does this change in speed help scientists "see" under the earth's crust? **Scientists can track the speed of earthquake waves under the crust. When the waves change speed, this tells the scientists that the material at that location is a different density. By tracking this, scientists can predict the thickness of the crust and the density of the magma below it.**

3. Why are earthquakes in the middle of the ocean so dangerous? **They trigger tsunamis that can kill people hundreds of miles away.**

Earthquake-proof buildings

1. What might architects do to help make buildings stronger? **Use reinforcing materials like rebar, overlap joints, and use strong materials.**

2. What shape of building is more likely to withstand an earthquake? **Short, broad buildings generally do better than tall, narrow designs.**

23. Detecting & Predicting Earthquakes

What did we learn?

1. What is the difference between the magnitude and the intensity of an earthquake? **Magnitude measures the actual strength of the earthquake—how strongly it moved the earth; intensity describes the damage done by the earthquake.**

2. What are three factors that determine how much damage is done by an earthquake? **Where it occurs, how strong it is, how long it lasts, how the buildings are built.**

3. Explain how a seismograph works. **The part with the rotating drum moves with the earth, and the part with the pen or light is attached to a mass that does not move with the earth.**

4. What people group was first to record earthquake measurements? **The Chinese about AD 132.**

Taking it further

1. What are some ways people have learned to prepare for earthquakes? **Buildings in areas that are prone to earthquakes are designed and built to be able to withstand vibrations. Also, scientists have an extensive network of seismographs and other instruments to detect earthquakes in hopes of giving enough advance warning for people to leave the area, although this has not proven very effective.**

2. What should you do if you are in an earthquake? **The best thing to do is get under something strong, like a sturdy table that can protect you from falling debris.**

24. Volcanoes

What did we learn?

1. What are the three stages or states of a volcano? **Active, dormant, extinct.**

2. Describe the three main parts of a volcano. **Magma chamber—area below crust filled with melted rock; central vent—channel through which magma forces its way to the surface; crater—indented area around the mouth of the volcano where a cone formed by solidified ash and lava has collapsed.**

3. Give the name for each of the following items that are emitted from a volcano:
   a. Liquid or melted rock: **Lava.**
   b. Tiny bits of solid rock: **Ash.**
   c. Pieces of rock from 0.2 to 1 inch (0.5–2.5 cm) in diameter: **Cinders.**
   d. Blobs of lava that solidify in the air: **Bombs.**
   e. Steam and carbon dioxide: **Gases.**

Taking it further

1. How might a volcano become active without anyone noticing? **If it is underwater or located in a very remote area.**

2. How are volcanoes and earthquakes related? **Both primarily occur where two tectonic plates meet and cause pressure to build up.**

3. How certain can we be that a volcano is really extinct? **Not completely. Several volcanoes have become active after being classified as extinct.**

25. Volcano Types

What did we learn?

1. What are the three shapes of volcanoes, and how is each formed? **Shield—mostly from lava; Cinder cone—mostly from solid debris such as ash and cinders; Composite—alternating between lava and solid matter.**

2. Where are most active volcanoes located today? **Along the Ring of Fire around the Pacific Ocean.**

3. What are some of the dangers of volcanoes? **Fire, debris, suffocation from gases, mudslides, tsunamis.**

4. What are some positive side effects of volcanoes? **Geothermal energy, sulfur deposits, fertile soil, new land, heat vents in the ocean, black sand beaches.**

Taking it further

1. How do black sand beaches form? **Black sand is formed when hot lava shatters as it cools very suddenly when reaching the ocean.**

26. Mount St. Helens

What did we learn?

1. Describe some of the ways the data collected at Mount St. Helens is challenging evolutionary thinking. **Canyons formed in only one day, 25 feet (7.6 m) of sedimentary layers laid down in only one day, upright trees on the bottom of Spirit Lake explain "petrified forests."**

Taking it further

1. How did the ash from the eruption of Mount St. Helens affect the weather in 1980? **It darkened the skies and cooled the temperatures, not just near the eruption site, but around the world.**

2. How could volcanic activity have contributed to the onset of the Ice Age? **Massive amounts of ash in the atmosphere would have blocked out much of the sunlight, causing cooler summers. Cooler temperatures combined with the large amount of water vapor from warm oceans would cause accumulation of snowfall leading to glacier formation.**

Volcano Word Search

A	D	O	P	X	Y	B	A	E	P	A	H	D	S	H
C	O	**D**	**O**	**R**	**M**	**A**	**N**	**T**	E	R	A	C	T	C
E	X	S	N	M	K	L	A	I	O	T	C	A	**E**	R
P	**A**	**H**	**O**	**E**	**H**	**O**	**E**	**A**	**S**	M	A	G	**R**	O
U	U	R	S	I	N	D	R	**C**	**H**	A	P	T	**U**	O
C	U	S	**U**	**B**	**D**	**U**	**C**	**T**	**I**	**O**	**N**	P	**P**	Q
O	A	U	L	I	N	S	**I**	**I**	E	E	C	R	**T**	E
M	**A**	**G**	**M**	**A**	O	M	**N**	V	L	X	Y	Z	**I**	O
P	L	M	K	R	**V**	Z	**D**	**E**	**D**	**T**	U	X	**O**	P
O	S	W	Q	B	O	**A**	**E**	L	I	**I**	F	F	**N**	A
S	C	L	**R**	**E**	**T**	**A**	**R**	**C**	A	**N**	P	O	S	T
I	T	S	U	I	O	**B**	**O**	**M**	**B**	**C**	S	H	I	L
T	C	N	E	D	R	**N**	H	F	R	**T**	W	K	L	J
E	C	**A**	**L**	**D**	**E**	**R**	**A**	E	T	X	N	T	M	I
R	W	I	O	P	R	Q	C	M	I	O	R	S	L	P

27. Geysers

What did we learn?

1. What are some ways that heated ground water shows up on the surface of the earth? **Hot springs and pools, spouters, fumaroles, mud pots, mud volcanoes and geysers.**

2. Explain how a geyser works. **Underground water is heated and expands inside a network of "plumbing." When the pressure of the heated water becomes greater than the weight of the water above it, it forces water up through the vent.**

3. How is a mud pot different from a hot spring? **A mud pot has more dirt than water in it, whereas a spring is mostly just water.**

Taking it further

1. How might a scientist figure out which irregular geysers are connected underground? **By observing the behavior of the geysers. If one becomes active at the same time another becomes inactive they might be connected.**

2. Why do some hot pools have a rainbow appearance? **The temperature of the water cools as it spreads out and different colored algae and bacteria grow in different temperatures of water.**

3. Can you tell the temperature of the water just by looking at a pool? **Maybe. Green-colored bacteria begin to grow in water just below 167° F (75° C). Other colors grow in lower temperatures; however, this may not be a completely accurate way to determine temperature.**

Challenge – Geothermal energy

1. Why are geothermal power plants mostly located near edges of tectonic plates? **Because that is where magma is most likely to find its way close to the surface of the earth.**

2. Would you expect geothermal power plants to experience more or fewer earthquakes than other power plants? **In general, you would expect more, because they are built in areas that have moving tectonic plates and are more likely to have earthquakes.**

3. Why is geothermal energy considered a renewable resource? **The magma and water are not being used up so there is a constant supply of steam. Even though**

water is "lost" to evaporation, it eventually condenses and returns to the ground through precipitation.

28. Weathering & Erosion

What did we learn?

1. What is weathering? **The wearing down of rocks by natural forces.**

2. Describe the two types of weathering. **Chemical— material is changed by chemical reactions; Mechanical—material is worn away by pressure from water/ice, wind, debris, plant roots.**

Taking it further

1. How does freezing and thawing of water break rocks? **Water expands when it freezes, breaking off bits of rock and enlarging the crack. After many cycles, the rock will break.**

2. In what ways do people use water or other materials to remove the surface of something in a process similar to mechanical weathering? **People use sand blasting to remove graffiti. Strip mining and dynamite are used to remove rock.**

Weathering worksheet

1. What did you observe as the vinegar came in contact with the limestone? **It should have fizzled.**

2. How did the limestone look afterward? **Some of the limestone should have been worn away.**

3. How did the dripping of the water affect the surface of the soap? **It should have caused a pit in the soap.**

4. How did the clay and straw change when the water froze? **The water expands as it freezes, either pushing out the clay or breaking the straw.**

5. What effects might freezing water have on rocks? **As water freezes it expands, widening cracks and breaking rocks apart.**

Challenge – Chemical Erosion worksheet

1. **Answers will vary.**

2. **Answers will vary.**

3. **Answers will vary.**

4. **Answers will vary.**

5. Why do you think this sample had the most rust? **You should have seen the most rust in the bag with both water and lots of air. Water removes (erodes) the rust from the iron and allows the air in the bag to react with more iron causing more oxidized iron atoms. The bag with water and no air had some rust because of small amounts of oxygen in the air left in the bag and dissolved in the water.**

29. Mass Wasting

What did we learn?

1. What is mass wasting? **The movement of large amounts of rocks and soil due to gravity.**

2. What is slow movement of the soil and rocks down a slope called? **Creep.**

3. What is rapid or sudden movement of the soil and rocks called? **A landslide.**

Taking it further

1. How does water affect mass wasting? **Water can loosen the bonds between the rocks and soil, allowing gravity to move them more easily.**

2. How might weathermen predict when the avalanche danger is high? **The danger might increase when snow suddenly builds up during a storm, when winds are high or when the temperatures begin to warm up. All of these factors can change the strength of the bonds of the snow on the side of the mountain. However, weathermen cannot accurately predict when and where a specific avalanche will occur.**

30. Stream Erosion

What did we learn?

1. What is the most powerful eroding force? **Moving water.**

2. How does gravity cause stream erosion? **Gravity pulls water downhill. The steeper the hill, the faster and more powerfully the water flows.**

3. What is the gradient of a river? **The difference in elevation between the headwaters, or source, and the mouth, or lowest point.**

Taking it further

1. Why are farmers concerned about soil erosion? **Topsoil is difficult to replace, so it must be protected to enable the farmers to grow good crops.**

2. What are some steps farmers take to prevent water from eroding their topsoil? **They plow crossways to the flow of the water; they alternate crops; they terrace steep areas.**

3. Besides water, what other natural force can erode topsoil? **Wind can blow it away.**

4. What can farmers do to protect their topsoil from wind erosion? **They can plant trees to block or break up the wind. They can plant shorter rows to keep the wind from blowing soil too far away.**

5. Why do lakes and reservoirs have to be dredged, emptied, and dug out periodically? **Water from incoming streams deposits silt and rocks in the bottom of the lake and eventually fills it up.**

31. Soil

What did we learn?

1. What are the major components of soil? **Sand, silt, clay, organic material (humus).**

2. What is the most important element in soil for encouraging plant growth? **Humus—decayed plant matter.**

Taking it further

1. What type of rocks would you expect to find near an area with sandy soil? **Quartz rocks.**

2. What type of rocks would you expect to find near an area with clay soil? **Feldspar and mica.**

3. How does a river that regularly floods, such as the Nile, restore lost topsoil? **Soil is washed into the river by the moving water. When it floods, much of this soil is moved out of the riverbed to the area around the river. As the floodwaters recede, the soil is left behind and can be used for farming.**

4. What are some ways that farmers restore nutrients to the soil? **Chemical fertilizers, animal waste, rotating crops, plowing under crops.**

Challenge – Permeability of Soil worksheet

1. Which sample had the highest permeability? **Sample 2 should have the highest permeability because it has the largest particles.**

2. Which had the lowest permeability? **Sample 4 should have the lowest permeability because it has the smallest particles.**

3. How did your unsifted sample (sample 1) compare to the sifted samples? **Sample 1 should be somewhere in between since it is a combination of the other three.**

4. How does particle size affect permeability? **The larger the particles the greater the porosity and thus the greater the permeability. In other words, the bigger the particles the more air space there is so the faster the water can flow through.**

32. Grand Canyon

What did we learn?

1. What is the main controversy between evolutionists and creationists concerning the formation of Grand Canyon? **Was it formed by a little water over a long period of time, or by a lot of water over a short period of time?**

2. What evidence shows radiometric dating methods to be unreliable? **Rocks at lower levels were dated younger by 100s of millions of years than rocks at higher levels.**

Taking it further

1. What event at the eruption of Mount St. Helens supports the biblical view of how Grand Canyon was formed? **A flood resulting from the eruption formed a canyon 100 feet (30 m) wide and 100 feet (30 m) deep through solid rock in only one day. A flood on a much larger scale would have much larger effects.**

2. How can scientists look at similar data and draw different conclusions? **Everyone has preconceived ideas, or presuppositions, that affect how he or she views the evidence. Evolutionists believe the earth is billions of years old, so they reject any theories that conflict with that idea. Creationists believe what the Bible says and interpret the evidence from that point of view.**

3. How can we know what to believe when scientists disagree? **We must trust what God says.**

33. Caves

What did we learn?

1. How are the beautiful formations in caves formed? **Calcite is dissolved in water as it passes through the limestone. As the water evaporates, it leaves the calcite behind, forming beautiful shapes inside the caves.**

2. What is a stalactite? **A formation in a cave that hangs from the ceiling.**

3. What is a stalagmite? **A formation in a cave that forms on the floor.**

Taking it further

1. What evidence do we have that formations in caves can develop rapidly? **Formation has been measured to be rapid in some wet caves. Also, bats and other animals have been found preserved in some stalactites and stalagmites.**

2. Why is it likely that calcite formations would have formed rapidly after the Flood? **Conditions would have been very wet inside the caves, with many minerals suspended or dissolved in the water.**

3. Besides in caves, where can calcite deposits be found? **Near geysers in places such as Yellowstone National Park.**

34. Rocks & Minerals Collection: Final Project

What did we learn?

1. What are the three types of rocks? **Igneous, sedimentary, and metamorphic.**

2. What is a native mineral? **One made from a pure element such as gold or silver.**

Taking it further

1. What are some of the greatest or most interesting things you learned from your study of our planet earth? **Accept reasonable answers.**

2. Read Genesis chapters 1 and 2. Discuss what was created on each day and how each part completes the whole. **Consider using the drawing lesson at answersingenesis.org/docs2002/oh20020301_112.asp to develop this topic.**

3. What earth science topic would you like to learn more about? **Have students research at the library or the AiG website and the Internet.**

Our Weather & Water —• Quizzes Answer Keys

Quiz 1. Atmosphere & Meteorology
Lessons 1–4

Short answer:

1. What does it mean to have a Christian view of weather? **It means to recognize that God designed weather to work the way it does and He controls it. Everything is not just random chance.**

2. Name three things you might find in a local weather report. **Forecasted temperatures and precipitation, actual temperatures and precipitation, location of weather fronts, record temperatures, weather across the country.**

3. What is the outermost part of the atmosphere called? **The exosphere.**

4. What three events recorded in the Bible drastically affected the surface of the earth? **Creation, Fall, and Flood.**

5. List three ways the atmosphere protects life on earth. **Protects us from the vacuum of space, protects from harmful radiation, protects from extreme temperatures, provides air to breathe.**

6. What are scientists called who study the atmosphere? **Meteorologists.**

7. What is temperature? **Measurement of the energy in the atmosphere.**

8. What causes air pressure? **Gravity pulling down on air molecules.**

9. What is absolute humidity? **The total amount of moisture in the air.**

10. What is relative humidity? **The ratio of the amount of moisture in the air to the total amount of moisture the air could hold at the current temperature.**

11. What is precipitation? **Moisture that falls from the atmosphere.**

12. What is the major cause of wind? **Heating of the air by the sun's rays.**

13. Weather occurs in which part of the atmosphere? **Troposphere.**

14. What happens to the atmospheric pressure as you go up in altitude? **The pressure goes down.**

Challenge questions

Short answer:

15. Name at least two Christian scientists from the past. **Sir Isaac Newton, Lord Kelvin, Blaise Pascal, Johannes Kepler, Carl Linneaus, Robert Boyle, Charles Babbage, Joseph Lister, Georges Cuvier, David Brewster, Louis Pasteur, James Clerk Maxwell.**

16. What is lapse rate with respect to the atmosphere? **The rate at which the temperature decreases as you increase in altitude.**

17. Name two gases that are lighter than air. **Hydrogen and helium.**

18. Briefly explain how each of the following contributes to weather formation.

    Sun: **Generates energy waves that heat up the earth.**

    Earth: **Absorbs heat from the sun and radiates it into the atmosphere.**

    Air: **Absorbs heat from the sun and the earth causing molecules to move around and changes air pressure creating wind and weather fronts.**

    Water: **Evaporation and condensation of water contributes to much of the weather we experience.**

19. Does temperature always decrease with altitude? Explain your answer. **No. Above the troposphere temperatures increase with altitude through the stratosphere, decrease with altitude in the mesosphere, and increase with altitude in the thermosphere.**

Quiz 2. Ancient Weather & Climate
Lessons 5–8

Match the term with its definition.

1. _**F**_ Conditions in the atmosphere at a given time

2. _**C**_ Average weather conditions over a long time

3. _**I**_ Very dry climate

4. _**A**_ Wet warm climate year round

5. _**H**_ How plants were watered in the beginning

6. _**B**_ Event believed to be triggered by the Flood

7. _**D**_ Trapping of heat in the earth's atmosphere

8. _E_ Increase in Earth's average temperature due to increased carbon dioxide

9. _J_ Climate with four distinct seasons

10. _G_ Climate with cooler winters than tropical areas

Mark each statement as either True or False.

11. _T_ Average global temperatures have increased in the past 150 years.

12. _F_ Carbon dioxide is the main cause of the greenhouse effect.

13. _F_ It has been proven that global warming is caused by man's actions.

14. _T_ The earth's climate was probably more uniformly tropical before the Flood.

15. _F_ The Flood did not change the earth very much.

16. _T_ The Bible indicates there may have been one landmass before the Flood.

17. _F_ The climate changes from day to day.

18. _T_ Deserts can be cold.

19. _T_ The monsoon brings rain to much of Southeast Asia.

20. _F_ We should just ignore global warming.

Challenge questions

Short answer:

21. Describe the Coriolis effect. **Circular air currents develop due to the rotation of the earth—primarily counter clockwise in the northern hemisphere and clockwise in the southern hemisphere.**

22. In an area that primarily experiences updrafts, would you expect the weather to be wet or dry? Why would you expect this? **Rising air increases precipitation so it would be wet.**

23. Explain how finding fossils of dinosaurs in Antarctica gives a clue to its past climate. **In order for dinosaurs to exist they need plants or other animals to eat, so the climate had to have been warm enough to support this kind of life.**

24. How could the climate in an area have changed quickly in the past? **The Genesis Flood caused many changes to the earth, which greatly affected the climate in a short period of time. In general, rapid climate changes do not occur; the Flood was a very unusual event.**

25. Give an example of how global warming could be a beneficial thing. **Longer growing seasons, increased precipitation, fewer deaths due to the cold, increased shipping in northern areas.**

Quiz 3. Clouds
Lessons 9–12

Fill in the blank with the correct term from below.

1. Water vapor enters the atmosphere primarily through _evaporation_.

2. The _water cycle_ describes how water is reused over and over.

3. _Precipitation_ is water that is leaving the atmosphere.

4. When water vapor condenses in the atmosphere it forms a _cloud_.

5. A bubble of warm moist air is called a _convection cell_.

6. _Stratus_ clouds form in layers or sheets.

7. Big fluffy clouds are called _cumulus_ clouds.

8. _Cirrus_ clouds are wispy and curly.

9. Clouds that are likely to produce rain are called _nimbus_ clouds.

10. _Hail_ is large frozen pellets of ice falling from the atmosphere.

11. Water that crystallizes in the clouds and falls to the earth is called _snow_.

12. As water droplets fall, they begin to _coalesce_, meaning they begin to combine with other droplets.

13. _Drizzle_ is tiny droplets of water too small to be called rain.

14. All snowflakes have _six_ sides.

15. _Cloud seeding_ is sometimes used to try to produce rain.

16. Only about _ten_ percent of all clouds produce precipitation.

17. It is called _transpiration_ when water vapor is released when a person breathes.

18. _Vaporization_ occurs when water is heated to the boiling point.

19. The _dew point_ is the point where air holds as much moisture as it can for the current temperature.

20. A long period of time without precipitation is called a _drought_.

Challenge questions

Mark each statement as either True or False.

17. _F_ The water table is the surface of a lake.

18. _T_ Water flows through permeable rock.

19. _T_ Fog is a cloud that touches the ground.

20. _F_ Radiation fog occurs on windy nights.

21. _T_ Coastal areas often experience advection fog.

22. _T_ Water droplets require a condensation nucleus to coalesce.

23. _T_ Upslope fog occurs near mountains.

24. _F_ Acid rain is a myth.

25. _T_ Rain water is naturally acidic.

26. _T_ A spring is formed when ground water finds its way out the side of a hill.

Quiz 4. Storms
Lessons 13–17

Choose the best answer for each question or statement.

1. _B_ Most weather is determined by the location and movement of _____.

2. _A_ When two air masses meet what do they form?

3. _D_ An air mass has uniform _____.

4. _C_ Which weather phenomenon keeps temperatures more even on the earth?

5. _A_ When the wind blows from the sea to the land it is called a _____.

6. _A_ Winds that blow straight up consistently are called _____.

7. _C_ About the highest altitude that thunderstorms can reach is _____.

8. _A_ God provides a way to return nitrogen to the soil through _____.

9. _D_ A spiraling cloud that does not touch the ground is called a _____.

10. _A_ Hurricanes lose power when they _____.

Challenge questions

Fill in the blank with the correct term from below.

11. Scientists measure _high altitude winds_ several times a day to determine where air masses are likely to move.

12. _Mountains_ and _large lakes_ are two geological features that can affect how weather fronts move.

13. Jet streams are stronger during the _winter_ than in the _summer_.

14. Jet streams play a role in the formation of _tornadoes_.

15. You should climb to higher ground in the event of a _flash flood_.

16. _Doppler_ radar is used to determine the speed and direction that a storm is moving.

17. _Phased array_ radar will be able to scan the atmosphere much more quickly than current radar.

18. _Hurricane Hunters_ fly their airplanes through hurricanes and other storms.

19. Weather satellites allow scientists to view all of a _hurricane_ at one time.

20. _TOTO_ was a portable weather station placed in the path of a tornado.

21. A _dropsonde_ is a portable weather station dropped into a hurricane.

22. Because of the jet stream it is often faster to fly from _west_ to _east_.

23. Explain the difference between the eye of the hurricane and the eyewall of the hurricane. **The eye of the hurricane is the very center where the winds are light. The eyewall of the storm is a wall of clouds surrounding the eye where the winds are the strongest.**

24. Explain how a dropsonde helps meteorologists. **A dropsonde is a canister of weather instruments dropped into a storm. It has a parachute and slowly falls through the clouds, sending wind, temperature, humidity, and pressure information to the National Hurricane Center.**

Quiz 5. Weather Information
Lessons 18–22

Mark each statement as either True or False.

1. _T_ A meteorologist is someone who studies the weather.

2. _F_ A barometer is used to measure temperature.

3. _F_ Air pressure goes up as you go up in altitude.

4. _T_ A psychrometer is used to measure relative humidity in the air.

5. _F_ All weather sayings are superstitious myths.

6. _T_ Meteorologists use many different instruments to understand the weather.

7. _T_ Wind direction can be shown by using a wind sock.

8. _T_ Weather satellites are very valuable tools for meteorologists.

9. _F_ Weather balloons are used to measure the weather on the ground.

10. _T_ Doppler radar can help detect severe storms more quickly than regular radar.

11. _T_ Computers are very important tools for meteorologists.

12. _F_ A weather station model is not useful for conveying information.

13. _T_ The National Weather Service helps local meteorologists make forecasts.

14. _F_ Weather forecasts were more accurate before computers were used.

15. _T_ You can collect weather data at home.

16. _F_ An anemometer shows wind direction.

17. _F_ With enough information anyone can predict the weather accurately.

18. _T_ Aircraft and ships are used to help collect weather data.

19. _T_ A rain gauge collects rain to show how much precipitation has fallen.

20. _T_ God ultimately controls the weather.

Challenge questions

Match the term with its definition.

21. _C_ Equivalent temperature if the air was dry and still

22. _B_ Calculation using temperature and relative humidity

23. _D_ Calculation using temperature and wind speed

24. _E_ Satellite stays over the same earth location

25. _A_ Satellite moves over the earth's poles

Short answer:

26. Pete is outside when the temperature is 40°F and the wind is blowing at 15 miles per hour. Polly is outside when the temperature is 30°F and the wind is blowing at 5 miles per hour. Who is likely to feel more comfortable? **Polly; Pete's apparent temp. is 22.4°F; Polly's apparent temp. is 26.9°F.**

27. Paul is outside when the temperature is 90°F and the relative humidity is 50%. Patty is outside when the temperature is 85°F and the relative humidity is 80%. Who is likely to feel more comfortable? **Paul; Paul's apparent temp. is 94.6°F; Patty's apparent temp. is 96.8°F.**

Quiz 6. Ocean Movements
Lessons 23–29

Fill in the blank with the correct term.

1. List the five oceans of the world. _**Pacific, Atlantic, Indian, Antarctic (or Southern), Arctic.**_

2. The _**monsoon**_ winds allowed trade routes to be established in the Indian Ocean.

3. The main mineral dissolved in seawater is _**salt.**_

4. There is more oxygen in the ocean near the surface because of _**algae**_ growing there.

5. The three main ways that the ocean moves are _**currents**_, _**tides**_, and _**waves**_.

6. Cold water is more _**dense**_ than warm water, so it sinks.

7. Land near cold water currents tends to have weather that is _**dry and cold**_.

8. A body of warm water in the Pacific Ocean that greatly affects weather is _**El Niño**_.

9. The highest point of a wave is called the _**crest**_.

10. The lowest point of a wave is called the _**trough**_.

Mark each statement as either True or False.

11. _**F**_ Water molecules are moved hundreds of miles across the ocean by waves.

12. _**T**_ Friction between the air and the water causes waves to form.

13. _**F**_ The highest part of a wave is called the trough.

14. _**T**_ A tsunami is a very dangerous wave.

15. _**T**_ Tides are a result of the gravitational pull of the moon.

16. _**T**_ A rip current can pull a swimmer far out to sea.

17. _**F**_ Erosion from waves is never harmful.

18. _**T**_ Movement of the ocean is beneficial for all life on earth.

19. _**T**_ Weather myths are often based on truth.

Challenge questions

Choose the best answer for each question or statement.

20. _**B**_ What field of science began with the Challenger Expedition in 1872?

21. _**A**_ How many volumes of information were published after the Challenger Expedition?

22. _**D**_ Which is not a method of desalination?

23. _**A**_ Where are the majority of desalination plants located?

24. _**C**_ Major surface currents combine to form these five major circulations.

25. _**B**_ Surface currents and prevailing winds rotate counterclockwise in the northern hemisphere due to this.

26. _**C**_ What scale is used to describe wind and waves in the open ocean?

27. _**A**_ What is the difference between high tide and low tide called?

28. _**D**_ What is a whirlpool caused by changing tides called?

29. _**C**_ What erosional land formation closes off the mouth of a bay?

Quiz 7. Sea Floor
Lessons 30–34

1. **Label the features of the ocean floor in the following diagram.**

   A. **Continent**

   B. **Continental shelf**

   C. **Continental slope**

   D. **Seamount**

   E. **Abyssal plain**

   F. **Island**

   G. **Guyot**

   H. **Trench**

Below, label each ocean zone. Write each plant or animal from the list below next to the zone in which you are most likely to find it.

2. 0 to 660 feet is the _**sunlit (or euphotic)**_ zone. **Shark, algae, coral, jellyfish, seaweed**

3. 660 to 3,300 feet is the _**twilight (or disphotic)**_ zone. **Octopus, bioluminescent fish, sponges**

4. 3,300 to 13,200 feet is the _**midnight (or aphotic)**_ zone. **Tubeworms, anglerfish, sea spider**

5. 13,200 feet and deeper is called the _**abyss**_. **Sea lilies**

6. Very deep canyons are called _**trenches**_. **No plants or animals listed**

Challenge questions

Mark each statement as either True or False.

7. _**F**_ Astronauts primarily study conditions under the ocean.

8. _**T**_ Researchers can live in the *Aquarius* underwater lab for long periods of time.

9. _**T**_ Researchers in *Aquarius* must undergo a decompression period before surfacing.

10. _**T**_ Ocean trenches are found in subduction zones.

11. _**F**_ Ocean trenches and ridges are found in the same areas.

12. _T_ The Mariana Trench is the lowest place on earth.

13. _F_ Most volcanic activity takes place on land.

14. _T_ Ocean vents are usually located near underwater volcanoes.

15. _F_ Coral reefs are proven to be hundreds of thousands of years old.

16. _T_ Coral reefs can grow very rapidly.

Our Universe → *Quizzes* Answer Keys

Quiz 1. Space Models & Tools
Lessons 1–4

Short answer:

1. What are the two ways the earth moves in space? **Rotates on axis, revolves around sun.**

2. Why does the earth experience seasons? **Its axis is tilted with respect to the sun.**

3. Why are seasons an indication of God's provision for man? **The seasons allow more of the earth to be cultivated for food.**

4. What was the main idea of the geocentric model? **The earth was the center of our solar system/universe.**

5. What is the main idea of the heliocentric model? **The sun is the center of our solar system.**

Mark each statement either True or False.

6. _F_ Scientists can prove where the earth came from.

7. _F_ Scientists have proven the big bang is true.

8. _T_ The Bible can tell us some things about astronomy.

9. _F_ The Bible can tell us everything about astronomy.

10. _T_ Gravity is the force that holds all planets in orbit.

11. _F_ Galileo invented the first telescope.

12. _T_ Heavier objects exert more gravity than lighter objects.

13. _T_ Closer objects exert more gravity than ones farther away.

14. _F_ The sun exerts more gravity on us than the earth does.

15. _T_ The Bible says that God's power can be seen in His creation.

Challenge questions

Short answer:

16. List at least one contribution that each of the following men made to the study of astronomy.

Nicolaus Copernicus: **Developed the Heliocentric Model of the solar system.**

Galileo: **First to use a telescope to study the heavens, discovered moons around Jupiter and rings around Saturn, supported Heliocentric Model.**

Sir Isaac Newton: **Defined the laws of gravitation, developed a reflecting telescope to reduce chromatic aberration.**

17. Why do scientists look for ways to make telescopes larger? **Larger telescopes gather more light and give brighter, clearer images.**

18. Explain briefly how the mirror of the Keck telescope is made. **The Keck telescope mirror consists of many hexagon shaped mirrors that fit together to form a very large mirror.**

Quiz 2. Outer Space
Lessons 5–10

Match the term with its definition.

1. _C_ Millions of stars rotating around a center

2. _L_ Name of our galaxy

3. _F_ Collection of planets orbiting the sun

4. _I_ A group of stars that form a picture

5. _B_ Star that doesn't move with respect to the earth's rotation

6. _A_ Unit of measurement for distances in space

7. _E_ An exploding star

8. _H_ Cloud of gas and dust in space

9. _K_ Scientific study of the universe/space

10. _M_ Superstitious belief that stars control the future

11. _D_ Gap between Mars and Jupiter

12. _G_ Balls of ice that orbit the sun

13. _J_ Piece of space debris that reaches the earth's surface

14. _O_ Piece of space debris that burns up in the atmosphere

15. _N_ What you can tell from a star's color

Short answer:

16. If a star has a blue color, is it hotter or cooler than our sun? **Hotter.**

17. What two things do we need to know to determine how far away a star is? **Brightness and amount of light emitted.**

18. Why do stars appear to move through the night sky? **Primarily earth's rotation (earth's revolution causes the starts to be in a different location from one night to the next).**

19. Explain how the number of meteorites found in fossil layers confirms that the earth is young. **If the earth was billions of years old we would expect to find hundreds of meteorites in the fossil layers, but only a few have actually been confirmed.**

Challenge questions

Short answer:

20. Where do many evolutionists believe new stars are formed? Why is this unlikely? **In nebulae. Gas is expanding not contracting in nebulae.**

21. What names are given on a star map for the lines that are projected from the equator and the prime meridian? **Celestial equator and prime hour circle.**

22. What is the most common evolutionary explanation for the origins of the universe? **Big bang theory.**

23. Give one possible explanation for the ability to see distant starlight in a young world. **Earth is at the center of the universe and more time passed at the outer regions while the universe was expanding during creation than passed on earth. Another possible answer is that the speed of light was faster in the past.**

24. What is a group of asteroids traveling in the same path called? **A family.**

25. Name three asteroids in the Trojan family. **Achilles, Hektor, Nestor, Agamemnon, Odysseus, Ajax, Diomedes, Antilochus, and Menelaus.**

26. Why does the existence of short-period comets indicate that the universe is young? **Comets only exist for a few thousand years and we do not have any evidence that new comets are being formed.**

27. What is the most likely explanation for the extinction of dinosaurs? **Failure to adapt to changed climate after the Flood.**

Quiz 3. Sun & Moon
Lessons 11–18

List the planets in our solar system in order from the closest to the sun outward. **Mercury, Venus, Earth, Mars, Jupiter, Saturn, Uranus, Neptune.**

Mark each statement as either True or False.

1. _F_ A lunar eclipse occurs when the moon blocks the light from the sun.

2. _T_ The energy from the sun is generated by a process similar to a hydrogen bomb.

3. _F_ Scientists can directly view the interior of the sun.

4. _F_ The aurora borealis is a result of sunspots.

5. _F_ A total solar eclipse causes the whole earth to become dark.

6. _T_ Animals may act like night is falling during a solar eclipse.

7. _T_ It is very dangerous to look at the sun even during a total eclipse.

8. _F_ Solar collectors work best if they are painted glossy white.

9. _T_ Solar cells convert the sun's rays into electricity.

10. _T_ The same side of the moon always faces the earth.

11. _F_ Maria are areas on the moon filled with water.

12. _T_ The moon does not generate its own light.

Fill in the blank with the correct term.

13. The moon is called a _full_ moon when it is on the opposite side of the earth from the sun.

14. The moon is called a _new_ moon when it is on the same side of the earth as the sun.

15. The main elements found in the sun are _hydrogen and helium_.

16. The _Capture_ Theory for the origin of the moon says that it originally orbited the sun but was dislodged and later came to orbit the earth.

Challenge questions

Match the term with its definition.

17. _B_ Squashed circle

18. _C_ Place in orbit closest to the sun

19. _G_ Place in orbit farthest from the sun

20. _J_ Center of a sunspot

21. _D_ Outer edge of a sunspot

22. _E_ Not concentrated

23. _F_ Plain filled with hardened basalt

24. _K_ Depression made by a meteorite

25. _I_ Valley on the moon

26. _A_ Side of the moon facing the earth

27. _L_ Side of the moon facing away from the earth

28. _H_ The side of the moon facing away from the sun

Short answer:

29. Explain why sunspots near the sun's equator move faster than the ones near the poles. **The sun is plasma not solid so all parts of the sun do not rotate at the same rate. The equator rotates faster than the poles so sunspots there move more quickly.**

30. List one problem that engineers must overcome in order to make solar energy more effective. **Possible problems include: sunlight is dispersed not concentrated, light is not evenly distributed around the earth, sunlight is more direct in the summer than in the winter.**

Quiz 4. Planets
Lessons 19–27

Planet	Terrestrial or Jovian	Atmosphere (Yes/No) If yes, what is it made of?	# of known moons	Rings (Yes/No)	Surface temp (Hot/Cold/ Comfortable)
Mercury	Terrestrial	Not much—very thin helium/ hydrogen	0	No	Hot and cold
Venus	Terrestrial	Yes—carbon dioxide/ nitrogen/sulfuric acid	0	No	Hot
Earth	Terrestrial	Yes—nitrogen/oxygen	1	No	Comfortable
Mars	Terrestrial	Yes—carbon dioxide	2	No	Comfortable to cold
Jupiter	Jovian	Yes—hydrogen	60+	Yes	Cold
Saturn	Jovian	Yes—hydrogen/helium	60+	Yes	Cold
Uranus	Jovian	Yes—hydrogen/helium/ methane	20+	Yes	Cold
Neptune	Jovian	Yes—hydrogen/helium/ methane	13	Yes	Cold
Pluto (dwarf planet)	Neither/ unknown	Possibly/Sometimes—very thin methane	5	No	Cold

2. If you could visit any of the planets, which would you choose and why? **Answers will vary.**

Challenge questions

1–3. **Mercury—has a slight atmosphere, has a magnetic field, is similar to our moon**
Venus—surface geography, temperature and pressure; Earth—not needed
Mars—Soil composition, surface geography, possible water ice
Jupiter—information on Great Red Spot
Saturn—shepherd moons, Enceladus's role in ring formation
Uranus and Neptune—discovery of moons
Pluto—tall mountains were discovered, no impact craters, actual pictures of Pluto and its moons.

Short answer:

4. Name two dwarf planets besides Pluto. **Ceres and Eris**

5. Explain why planets that are closer to the sun orbit more quickly than those that are farther away. **The gravity of the sun exerts a force on each planet, causing it to move in a circular path around the sun. The closer the planet is to the sun the stronger the gravitational pull is. This stronger force causes the planet to move more quickly.**

Quiz 5. Space Program
Lessons 28–33

Choose the best answer for each question.

1. _B_ At this time, what is the best way to study long-term effects of zero-gravity?

2. _A_ Which characteristic is generally not a quality of an astronaut?

3. _D_ What was designed to protect astronauts in space?

4. _C_ What wartime invention led to space exploration?

5. _A_ What object was launched into space on Oct. 4, 1957?

6. _B_ Who was the first man in space?

7. _C_ Who challenged America to put a man on the moon before 1970?

8. _A_ Which of the following is not a function of space satellites?

9. _D_ Which of the following programs did not help to put a man on the moon?

10. _B_ What rocket was used in the Apollo space program?

11. _C_ Who was the first person to walk on the moon?

12. _C_ Which of the following was not left on the moon?

13. _D_ What shape was the shuttle orbiter?

14. _B_ What was the maximum number of crew members on the space shuttle?

Challenge questions

Short answer:

15. Choose one of the astronauts you have learned about and explain what you admire about him/her. **Answers will vary.**

16. List three ways that NACA helped improve flight. **Improved air foils, engines, and wings, safety improvements, ice reduction processes, hypersonic and supersonic designs.**

17. List three challenges unique to living and working in space. **No gravity, no air, no air pressure, no heat and cold protection, radiation.**

18. Why is private space research important? **Competition spurs innovation; commercial applications will help support further research; improvements in space research can be applied to other areas of life; private space research looks at areas that are not funded by the government so improvements are made in more areas.**

19. What is the purpose of the Orion spacecraft? **To carry people to the moon and farther into outer space, perhaps one day to Mars.**

20. In what ways is the Orion system similar to the Apollo system? **It has a cone shaped crew module and a service module.**

21. What is one fascinating thing you have learned? **Answers will vary.**

Our Planet Earth ⚷ *Quizzes* Answer Keys

Quiz 1. Origins & Glaciers
Lessons 1–7

Mark each statement as either True or False.

1. _T_ We can rely on the Bible to tell us the truth about God and His creation.

2. _F_ We can prove scientifically where the earth came from.

3. _F_ Science can answer all of our questions.

4. _T_ Fossils have been located in every part of the world.

5. _T_ The biblical account of the Flood explains much of what we see on earth.

6. _F_ A scientist should disregard evidence that contradicts his/her theories.

7. _T_ Scientists have not proven evolution to be true.

8. _T_ The abundance of aquatic fossils is consistent with a worldwide flood.

9. _T_ The worldwide flood was God's punishment for man's sin.

10. _T_ Evolutionists cannot adequately explain how conditions formed to create an ice age.

Short answer:

11. List three biblical events that greatly affected the surface of the earth. **Creation, Fall, Flood.**

12. Describe three attributes of the earth that make it just right for life to occur here. **Distance from sun, tilt of axis, properties and abundance of water, oxygen/nitrogen ratio, size provides just the right amount of gravity.**

13. List three ways that geology affects your life. **Minerals in food, anything made of metal, oil, anything made of plastic, soil to grow plants, caves to explore, etc.**

14. List the two climate conditions required for an ice age. **Wet winters and cool summers.**

15. List the four main studies of earth science. **Astronomy, meteorology, geology, hydrology.**

Challenge questions

Short answer:

16. Explain what the following quote is saying about scientists who believe in evolution.

Dr. Scott Todd, an immunologist at Kansas State University: "Even if all the data point to an intelligent designer, such an hypothesis is excluded from science because it is not naturalistic." **Evolutionists will ignore the data if they point to a Creator.**

17. Based on what you have learned about the great Ice Age, in which areas would you expect to see evidence of glaciers? Write yes if you would expect to see it and no if you would not expect to see it.

   A. _**Yes**_ Canada

   B. _**Yes**_ Montana

   C. _**No**_ Mexico

   D. _**Yes**_ Norway

   E. _**Yes**_ Siberia

   F. _**No**_ Egypt

18. List three economic or social effects caused by the Little Ice Age. **Changes in fishing grounds; changes in the crops that could be grown; some people had to move as glaciers advanced; less food was available so some people suffered from famine, etc.**

Quiz 2. Rocks & Minerals
Lessons 8–18

Choose the best answer for each question.

1. _B_ What percentage of all fossils are fossilized dinosaur bones?

2. _A_ What rock is commonly used for buildings and monuments?

3. _C_ Which of the following is required in order for a plant or animal to fossilize?

4. _A_ What rock is made from the same element as diamonds?

5. _B_ Why should we be careful when using the results of carbon-14 dating?

6. _C_ What is one common characteristic of metamorphic rock?

7. _A_ How many elements are in a native mineral?

8. _B_ What is a common mineral found in the human body?

9. _D_ Which of the following is a native mineral?

10. _D_ How are artificial gems easily identified?

Short answer:

11. Where is the earth's crust the thickest? **Earth's crust is thickest under the mountains.**

12. Name the three types of rocks. Describe how each type is formed and give an example of each.

   A. **Igneous—formed when melted rock cools. Examples: pumice, basalt, obsidian, granite.**

   B. **Sedimentary—formed from small bits of broken rock, shells, and other materials that are cemented together, or when minerals precipitate out of water. Examples: sandstone, mudstone, shale, limestone, dolomite.**

   C. **Metamorphic—formed when igneous or sedimentary rocks are changed by pressure and heat over time. Examples: marble, slate, gneiss, quartzite.**

Challenge questions

Match the term with its definition.

13. _C_ The most common element in the earth's crust

14. _E_ Most common rock in continental crust

15. _G_ Most common rock in oceanic crust

16. _H_ Holes found in igneous rocks

17. _A_ Rock containing two or more sizes of crystals

18. _I_ Fragmental rock with rounded clasts

19. _B_ Fragmental rock with angular clasts

20. _J_ Fossilized animal dung

21. _D_ Mineral with atoms of only one type

22. _F_ Mineral with two or more elements in definite proportions

23. _L_ Order of rock layers according to evolutionists

24. _K_ Smooth stones found inside fossilized animal bodies

25. What are three sources for moon rocks that are now on earth? **American astronauts, unmanned soviet probes, meteorites from the moon**

26. What is the difference between a rock and a mineral? **A mineral is a native element or compound. It contained only one kinds of substance. A rock is a mixture of different minerals mixed together.**

Quiz 3. Mountains & Movement
Lessons 19–26

Match the term with its definition.

1. _F_ Theory that the crust is composed of several large landmasses

2. _C_ Name given to original landmass

3. _H_ Series of mountain peaks in a given area

4. _I_ Highest mountain peak on earth

5. _E_ Center of earthquake activity

6. _L_ Smaller quakes after a major earthquake

7. _N_ The Richter scale measures this

8. _D_ Instrument for measuring earthquakes

9. _O_ Blobs of lava that harden in the air

10. _B_ A volcano that has not erupted in the past 50 years

11. _M_ A volcano that is not expected to erupt again

12. _G_ Volcano that recently erupted in Washington State

13. _J_ Volcano that had one of the largest eruptions ever

14. _K_ Type of volcano formed from lava and solid material

15. _A_ One tectonic plate sliding under another

Short answer:

16. Explain the difference between the elevation of a mountain and its actual height. **The elevation is the height of the summit above sea level. The actual height is the difference between the elevation of the summit and the elevation of the base of the mountain.**

Challenge questions

Mark each statement as either True or False.

17. _T_ Continental drift is the name given to the movement of tectonic plates.

18. _F_ Rifting occurs when two tectonic plates collide.

19. _F_ There are relatively few mountain ranges in the world.

20. _T_ Pressure on tectonic plates can cause rocks to fold or bend.

21. _T_ An anticline is formed when rocks bend upward.

22. _F_ A hanging wall is the rock layers below a fault.

23. _T_ A hanging wall moves downward in a normal fault.

24. _F_ Most earthquakes and volcanoes are located around the Atlantic Ocean.

25. _T_ Continental flood basalts are an indication of catastrophic plate movement in the past.

26. _T_ Scientists cannot accurately predict when a volcano will erupt.

Quiz 4. Water & Erosion
Lessons 27–34

Fill in the blank with the correct term from below.

1. A thermal feature that shoots hot water many feet into the air is a _**geyser**_.

2. _**Old Faithful**_ is one of the most famous geysers in the world.

3. _**Geothermal**_ energy can be obtained from areas containing geysers.

4. Geysers often contain _**hydrogen sulfide**_, which gives them a bad smell.

5. A _**fumarole**_ is produced when super-heated steam reaches the surface.

6. The process of wearing down rocks is called _**weathering**_.

7. _**Frost heaving**_ is the process that brings rocks to the surface each winter.

8. _**Mass wasting**_ is the effect of gravity pulling soil and rocks down a hill.

9. Rapid movement of large amounts of rocks and soil is called a _**landslide**_.

10. The most powerful eroding force is _**moving water**_.

11. The most important component of soil for growing plants is _**humus**_.

12. _**Ash**_ can become fertile soil after a volcanic eruption.

13. A formation in a cave that goes from floor to ceiling is called a _**column**_.

14. _**Gravity**_ is the force that causes water to move rapidly down a hill.

15. _**Limestone**_ is the main type of rock from which caves are formed.

Short answer:

16. Explain the process that causes a geyser to erupt. **Water fills twisting chambers underground. Magma heats the water that is deep in the ground. This superheated water expands and builds up pressure. When the pressure below is greater than the weight of the water above, the geyser erupts.**

Challenge questions
Short answer:

17. Where is the most likely place to find geothermal areas? **Near the boundaries of tectonic plates.**

18. List two types of chemical erosion. **Acids, water, oxidation.**

19. Which is more easily eroded: iron or rust? **Rust.**

20. Where are rock glaciers likely to be located? **Steep mountain slopes with cool summers (Colorado and Alaska).**

21. What is a fossil rock glacier? **A rock glacier that no longer has any ice in it.**

22. Which has more power to erode: fast-moving water or slow-moving water? **Fast-moving water.**

23. What is porosity in soil? **The measure of the amount of air space in the soil.**

24. What is permeability of soil? **The speed at which water flows through a sample of soil.**

25. Why are porosity and permeability important? **They affect how well plants will grow in the soil.**

26. What are two indications of a large scale flood found in Grand Canyon? **Two hundred miles of level sedimentary layers, abundant aquatic fossils, nautiloid fossils all lined up the same way, fossilized amphibian and reptile footprints in sandstone.**

Our Weather & Water —o Final Exam Answer Keys

Lessons 1–34

Fill in the blank with the correct term from below.

1. _Meteorology_ is the study of the earth's atmosphere.

2. _Climate_ is the average weather conditions in an area over a long period of time.

3. The Genesis Flood set up environmental conditions just right for an _ice age_.

4. A _glacier_ can form when snow does not completely melt in the summer.

5. Water vapor that condenses in the air forms _clouds_.

6. Water that falls from the sky is called _precipitation_.

7. The _sun_ is responsible for most of the winds we experience on earth.

8. Hurricanes can only form near the _equator_.

9. The _computer_ is the most important piece of equipment for analyzing weather.

10. Weather fronts form where two _air masses_ meet.

Analyze the weather station model and fill in the blanks.

11. Temperature: **32°F**

12. Wind speed: **15 knots**

13. Wind direction: **North**

14. Precipitation: **Snow**

15. Cloud cover: **100%**

16. Air pressure: **1020.1 millibars**

Mark each statement as either True or False.

17. _F_ Relative humidity is the total amount of water vapor in the air.

18. _T_ Meteorologists use computers to help them forecast the weather.

19. _T_ The oceans play an important role in the weather.

20. _F_ El Niño is a wind in South America.

21. _T_ The ocean contains many minerals and gases in addition to water.

22. _T_ Ocean currents are sometimes a result of different amounts of salt in the water.

23. _T_ Energy from waves can be used to make electricity.

24. _F_ Waves are always helpful.

25. _F_ Tides are lower when the sun and the moon line up.

26. _F_ Most plants and animals are found in the twilight zone of the ocean.

Match the term with its definition.

27. _B_ Very deep valley in the ocean floor

28. _E_ Very hot water coming up through sea floor

29. _C_ Large collection of colonies of polyps

30. _H_ Vehicle for deep-sea exploration

31. _F_ Animal that can glow in the dark

32. _A_ Largest ocean on earth

33. _G_ Organism that produces most of the oxygen in the ocean

34. _D_ Strong current moving water from the shore to the open sea

35. _I_ Area where most plants and animals live in the ocean

Challenge questions

36. Use the following words to label the diagram of the atmosphere with the correct levels.

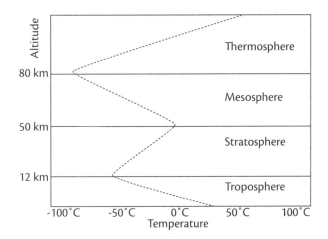

37. What are the four "ingredients" needed to make weather? **Earth, water, air, and sun.**

38. Explain how we get clues to what the climate was like in the past. **We get clues from fossils. The types of plants and animals found in an area can give us clues as to what the climate must have been like in order for those plants and animals to have lived there.**

39. List three kinds of fog. **Radiation, advection, steam, valley, upslope.**

40. What are two ways that acid rain can form? **Naturally—carbon dioxide in the atmosphere dissolves to create carbonic acid; chemically—sulfur and nitrogen compounds enter the air through pollution and dissolve in the water vapor to form sulfuric acid and nitric acid.**

41. The jet stream is most affected by the difference in temperature between which areas of the world? **Equator and the Poles.**

42. Name two kinds of radar that are used to detect severe weather. **Doppler, phased array.**

43. Explain how someone outside in the winter could feel more comfortable in a colder temperature than he or she does when the outside temperature is warmer. **The wind makes it feel colder because it increases the rate at which sweat evaporates, so if the wind is blowing more on a warmer day you could actually feel colder than if it blowing less on a colder day.**

44. What are two methods for desalinating ocean water? **Distillation, reverse osmosis.**

Our Universe ⎯⎯• Final Exam Answer Keys

Lessons 1–34

Fill in the blank with the correct term from below.

1. An _asteroid_ is a chunk of rock in a regular orbit around the sun.

2. The surface of the moon is covered with dark areas called _maria_.

3. A piece of space debris that burns up in the earth's atmosphere is a _meteor_.

4. Space _probes_ can explore areas that man cannot.

5. A piece of space debris that hits the earth's surface is a _meteorite_.

6. A _supernova_ is a star that experiences a very large explosion.

7. A _comet_ is a ball of ice and dust that orbits the sun.

8. A star that has exploded and collapsed in on itself is called a _black hole_.

9. An _eclipse_ occurs when one heavenly body blocks the light from another heavenly body.

10. The gases surrounding a planet are its _atmosphere_.

11. A large cloud of gas and dust in space is a _nebula_.

12. Heated plasma that extends from the surface of the sun to 6,200 miles is the _chromosphere_.

13. The _corona_ is the outermost part of the sun's atmosphere.

14. The visible surface of the sun is called the _photosphere_.

15. _Solar energy_ is energy from the sun.

16. A _satellite_ is anything that has a regular orbit around a planet.

Short answer:

17. List at least one unique characteristic for each planet (or plutoid). **Accept any reasonable answer.**

    Mercury—Closest to the sun, little or no atmosphere, no moons, extreme temperatures.

Venus—Sulfuric acid clouds, hottest planet in the solar system, closest in size to earth.

Earth—Only planet with life, significant amount of water, designed by God for us.

Mars—Red planet, frozen carbon dioxide at the poles, most space probes.

Jupiter—Largest planet, Great Red Spot, gas giant.

Saturn—Beautiful rings, second largest planet, gas giant.

Uranus—Rotates on its side, blue color.

Neptune—Methane atmosphere gives it a blue color, had the Great Dark Spot.

Pluto—Former planet, classified as a dwarf planet, Charon in synchronous orbit.

18. Describe why gravity is important to our solar system. **Gravity holds everything in place. It makes the planets orbit the sun. It makes the moons orbit the planets. It holds our atmosphere in place.**

19. Place these colors of stars in order from coolest to hottest: blue, orange, yellow, white. **Orange, yellow, white, blue.**

20. What are the two ways that planets move through space? **Rotate on axis, revolve around the sun.**

21. List three tools used to study space. **Space probe, space ships, space station, satellite, telescopes.**

22. What was the purpose of the Apollo missions? **To send a man to the moon.**

23. Why was the space shuttle developed? **To make a reusable space ship, to do research in orbit.**

24. What is the purpose of the International Space Station? **To have a place to conduct long-term micro-gravity experiments.**

25. List three purposes of a space suit. **To protect the astronaut from harmful radiation and extreme temperature, to provide pressure and air, to provide communications.**

Challenge questions

Mark each statement as either True or False.

26. _T_ A Foucault pendulum demonstrates the rotation of the earth.

27. _F_ Kepler was the first to suggest the heliocentric model of the universe.

28. _F_ Distant starlight proves the universe is billions of years old.

29. _T_ The celestial equator on a star map corresponds to the equator on a map of the earth.

30. _T_ Sir Isaac Newton improved on Galileo's design of the early telescope.

31. _T_ The larger the opening of a telescope, the more you can magnify the image.

32. _T_ Hektor and Achilles are two asteroids in the Trojan asteroid family.

33. _F_ Science has proven that a meteor led to the extinction of the dinosaurs.

34. _T_ Kepler's laws of planetary motion explain why planets move in ellipses.

35. _F_ Solar flares are unrelated to sunspots.

36. _F_ All planets are at the same tilt with respect to the sun.

37. _T_ There are four Jovian and four terrestrial planets.

38. _T_ Mercury and Venus have very different atmospheres from earth.

39. _T_ More space probes have gone to Mars than to any other planet.

40. _F_ SpaceShipOne proved that private space research is unrealistic.

41. _T_ Orion is being modeled after the Apollo program.

42. _F_ Only official astronauts are allowed on the International Space Station.

43. _T_ Most astronauts have had a military background.

44. _F_ The International Space Station was assembled in Florida.

45. _T_ *Apollo 13* astronauts used ingenuity to solve problems in space after an explosion.

Our Planet Earth ➔ Final Exam Answer Keys

Lessons 1–34

Label this diagram of the earth.

A. **Crust**   B. **Mantle**   C. **Outer Core**   D. **Inner Core**

Mark each statement as either True or False.

1. _T_ Scientists "see" beneath the crust of the earth using earthquake (seismic) waves.

2. _F_ The core is the coolest part of the earth.

3. _T_ Magma is liquid rock under the surface of the earth.

4. _F_ Coal is not a rock because it is organic.

5. _F_ Rocks never change form.

6. _T_ Rocks are made from one or more minerals or organic materials.

7. _T_ Larger crystals form in igneous rock if it is cooled slowly.

8. _F_ All rocks sink in water.

9. _T_ Sandstone is a sedimentary rock.

10. _T_ Limestone frequently contains fossils.

11. _F_ Fossils prove that evolution is true.

12. _F_ Fossils prove that creation is true.

13. _T_ Natural gas is almost always found near oil deposits.

14. _F_ Metamorphic rock can form at low temperatures.

Fill in the blank with the correct term from below.

15. The _**1st law of thermodynamics**_ states that matter cannot be created or destroyed.

16. The _**2nd law of thermodynamics**_ states that all systems tend toward a state of chaos.

17. Most _**evolutionists**_ believe that everything in nature happened only by natural processes.

18. _**Uniformitarianism**_ is the belief that everything was formed by the slow processes we observe today.

19. A _**glacier**_ is a thick sheet of ice that does not completely melt each summer.

20. _**Erosional**_ mountains are formed as wind and water erode material away.

21. _**Depositional**_ mountains are formed as layers of sediment are deposited.

22. One of the most dangerous side effects of an earthquake is a _**tsunami**_.

23. When stress due to moving tectonic plates is released it often causes an _**earthquake**_.

24. _**Indonesia**_ is one of the most active volcanic countries in the world.

25. The difference between the base and the peak of a mountain is its _**height**_.

26. The difference between sea level and the peak of a mountain is its _**elevation**_.

Short answer:

27. List two methods used by farmers to reduce soil erosion. **Terracing, crop rotation, plowing across flow of water, wind breaks, or ground cover.**

28. The evolutionist view of Grand Canyon is **lots** of time, **little bit** of water.

29. The creationist view of Grand Canyon is **little bit** of time, **lots** of water.

30. Describe the process for the eruption of a geyser. **Water fills underground passages and is heated by magma. When the pressure of the expanded water is greater than the weight of the water above it, the water is forced upward out of the vent.**

31. Explain how water can break a rock. **Water fills a crack then expands as it freezes, making the crack larger. Then the water melts. This process is repeated**

over and over until the rock breaks. **Moving or running water can also wear away at a rock until it breaks.**

Challenge questions

Match the term with its definition.

32. _A_ Lithification

33. _E_ Clasts

34. _J_ Matrix

35. _B_ Striations

36. _C_ Terminal morain

37. _H_ Glacial erratic

38. _D_ Syncline

39. _L_ Foot wall

40. _F_ Hanging wall

41. _G_ Oxidation

42. _I_ Porosity

43. _K_ Permeability

Short answer:

44. Explain how Mount St. Helens provides evidence that supports the Bible. **Mount St. Helens shows that large amounts of sedimentary rock could form in a short period of time, and water can form canyons in a short period of time. Both support the biblical idea of a young earth. Spirit Lake shows how trees could become fossilized vertically. All of this supports the idea of a large-scale catastrophe (like a global flood) causing many of the features we see today.**

45. Explain how Grand Canyon provides evidence that supports the Bible. **Grand Canyon has many folded rock layers that indicate they were formed quickly and folded while still pliable. This supports the idea of a large flood, not millions of years. Many rock layers are formed on top of very large, flat lower layers, again supporting the idea of a flood. Fossilized footprints indicate there was a catastrophe that covered them quickly.**

Appendices

for Use with

God's Design: Heaven & Earth

Our Weather & Water Master Supply List

The following table lists all the supplies used for *God's Design for Heaven & Earth: Our Weather & Water* activities. You will need to look up the individual lessons in the student book to obtain the specific details for the individual activities (such as quantity, color, etc.). The letter "*c*" denotes that the lesson number refers to the challenge activity. Common supplies such as colored pencils, construction paper, markers, scissors, tape, etc., are not listed.

Supplies needed (see lessons for details)	Lesson
☐ Aquarium or other empty glass case	31
☐ Baking dish	4
☐ Balloons	3
☐ Bible	35
☐ Bottle with lid	22, 28
☐ Candle	2
☐ Cotton balls	11
☐ Dry ice	10c
☐ Duct tape	16, 22
☐ Flour	12
☐ Food coloring	4, 13, 22, 25
☐ Global warming articles	8
☐ Gloves	10c
☐ Graph paper	2c, 21c
☐ House plant	6
☐ Ice	10
☐ Jar with lid	2, 3c, 10, 19, 25, 26, 28
☐ Masking tape	3, 4, 14, 19, 26
☐ Matches	2, 11c
☐ Metal clothes hanger	14
☐ Mirror	6
☐ Modeling clay	2, 22, 29, 31, 34
☐ Newspaper	1, 5, 21
☐ Paint roller pan	28
☐ pH testing paper (optional)	12c
☐ Piece of cloth	15, 18

Supplies needed (see lessons for details)	Lesson
☐ Plastic bottle (empty, 2-liter)	11c, 13, 16, 22, 26
☐ Plastic grocery bag	3c
☐ Plastic tornado tube (optional but recommended)	16
☐ Plastic tubing (clear)	22
☐ Plastic zipper bag	10
☐ Playing cards	30
☐ Poster board/tagboard	22
☐ Rubber band	18
☐ Salt	24
☐ Sand	19, 28
☐ Shoeboxes	10c
☐ Short ruler (6-inch)	22
☐ Sling psychrometer (optional)	18
☐ Slinky	26
☐ Straw	22
☐ String	3, 12, 22, 26
☐ Stuffed animal	15
☐ Styrofoam™ cups	4
☐ Syrup	13
☐ The Magic School Bus on the Ocean Floor	29
☐ Thermometer	18
☐ Trash bag (large)	14
☐ Weather station (optional)	22
☐ Wooden stick (small, skewer-like)	22
☐ World atlas/map	5, 23
☐ Yard stick/meter stick	3

Our Weather & Water Resource Guide

Suggested Books

Weather and the Bible by Donald B. DeYoung—One hundred questions on weather-related topics are answered from the Christian perspective

Life in the Great Ice Age by Michael and Beverly Oard—Learn what life was like during the Ice Age after the Flood in this colorful novel

The New Weather Book by Michael Oard—From the practical to the pretty amazing, this book gives essential details into understanding what weather is, how it works, and how other forces impact it

The New Ocean Book by Frank Sherwin—You'll be amazed by what lies beneath the surface of the world's oceans!

The Magic School Bus on the Ocean Floor by Joanna Cole—Fun and informative book

The Magic School Bus Inside a Hurricane by Joanna Cole—Fun way to learn about storms

Frozen in Time by Michael Oard—Explanation of woolly mammoth finds

Suggested Videos

Newton's Workshop by Moody Institute—Excellent Christian science series; several titles to choose from

Global Warming—A documentary from Answers in Genesis on the science and politics surrounding global warming

Awesome Forces of God's Creation—Three-DVD set from Moody, includes *Roaring Waters*, *Thundering Earth*, and *Whirling Winds*

Field Trip Ideas

- Creation Museum in Petersburg, Kentucky
- Check if your area power company has wind-generating equipment; set up a tour
- Beach (if one is nearby)
- Local weather station
- Visit a scuba diving school

Creation Science Resources

Answers Book for Kids Eight volumes by Ken Ham with Cindy Malott—Answers children's frequently asked questions

The New Answers Books 1–4 by Ken Ham and others—Answers frequently asked questions

The Amazing Story of Creation by Duane T. Gish—Gives scientific evidence for the creation story

Creation Science by Felice Gerwitz and Jill Whitlock—Unit study focusing on creation

Creation: Facts of Life by Gary Parker—Comparison of the evidence for creation and evolution

The Young Earth by John D. Morris—Lots of facts disproving old-earth ideas

Our Weather & Water Works Cited

"Acid Rain." http://www.epa.gov/acidrain/index.html.

Ardley, Neil. *The Science Book of Weather*. San Diego: Gulliver Books, 1992.

"Ashkelon Desalination Plane, Seawater Reverse Osmosis (SWRO) Plant, Israel." http://www.water-technology.net/projects/israel/.

"Benjamin Franklin." http://web.lemoyne.edu/~giunta/franklin.html.

Brice, Tim. "Heat Index." http://www.srh.noaa.gov/elp/wxcalc/heatindex.shtml.

"California's Rocky Intertidal Zones." http://ceres.ca.gov/ceres/calweb/coastal/rocky.html.

Cobb, Allan B. *Weather Observation Satellites*. New York: Rosen Publishing Group, 2003.

"Colorado Remembers Big Thompson Canyon Flash Flood of 1976." http://www.noaanews.noaa.gov/stories/s688.htm.

Conjecture Corp. "What is the Jet Stream?" http://www.wisegeek.com/what-is-the-jet-stream.htm.

Coutsoukis, Photius. "Russian Climate." http://www.photius.com/countries/russia/climate/russia_climate_climate.html.

Daly, John L. "The El Niño Southern Oscillation." http://www.john-daly.com/elnino.htm.

Demarest, Chris L. *Hurricane Hunters! Rides on the Storm*. New York: Margaret K. McElderry Books, 2006.

DeYoung, Donald B. *Weather & the Bible*. Grand Rapids: Baker Book House, 1996.

"El Niño Warm Water Pool Decreasing." http://visibleearth.nasa.gov/view_rec.php?id=542.

Fleisher, Paul. *Coral Reef*. New York: Benchmark Books, 1998.

"Fog." http://www.bbc.co.uk/weather/features/understanding/fog.shtml.

Fredericks, Anthony D. *Exploring the Oceans—Science Activities for Kids*. Golden: Fulcrum Resources, 1998.

Gardiner, Brian. *Energy Demands*. London: Gloucester Press, 1990.

Gardner, Robert. *Science Project Ideas About Rain*. Berkely Heights: Enslow Publishers, Inc., 1997.

Gibbons, Gail. *Exploring the Deep, Dark Sea*. Boston: Little, Brown and Company, 1999.

Gray, Susan H. *Coral Reefs*. Minneapolis: Compass Point Books, 2001.

Harper, Suzanne. *Clouds: From Mares Tails to Thunderheads*. New York: Franklin Watts, 1997.

Haslam, Andrew, and Barbara Taylor. *Make It Work Weather*. Chicago: World Book, 1997.

"Intertidal Zones." http://neptune.spaceports.com/~marine/life.html.

Jones, Lorraine. *Super Science Projects About Weather and Naturals Forces*. New York: Rosen Central, 2000.

"Joseph Priestly, The King of Serendipity." http://home.nycap.rr.com/useless/priestly/priestly.html.

Kahl, Jonathan D. *Storm Warning: Tornadoes and Hurricanes*. Minneapolis: Lerner Publications Co., 1993

Lambert, David. *Weather*. New York: Franklin Watts, 1983.

Low, Anne Marie. "Dust Bowl Diary." http://chnm.gmu.edu.

Meltzer, Milton. *Benjamin Franklin The New American*. New York: Franklin Watts, 1988.

Mulfinger, George, and Donald E. Snyder. *Earth Science for Christian Schools*. Greenville: Bob Jones University Press, 1995.

National Wildlife Federation. *Wild About Weather*. Philadelphia: Chelsea House Publishers, 1997.

"New Detection System Listens for Tornadoes." *Windsor Tribune*. 27 May 2003.

Oard, Michael. "Human-caused Global Warming Slight So Far." http://www.answersingenesis.org/articles/aid/v1/n1/human-caused-global-warming.

Oard, Michael, and Beverly Oard. *Life in the Great Ice Age*. Colorado Springs: Master Books, 1993.

Oard, Michael. *The Weather Book*. Green Forest: Master Books, 2000.

"Ocean Currents." http://seawifs.gsfc.nasa.gov/OCEAN_PLANET/ HTML/oceanography_currents_1.html.

"Ocean Exploration and Undersea Research Hydrothermal Vents." http://www.research.noaa.gov/oceans/t_vents.html.

Oxlade, Chris. *Weather*. Austin: Raintree Steck-Vaughn, 1999.

"Quick Bits of 'L.'" *Tidbits*. 8 October 2003: 2.

"Saltwater Desalination in California." http://www.coastal.ca.gov/ desalrpt/dchap1.html.

Sands, Stella. "Tornadoes." *Kids Discover*. June/July 1996: 1–20.

Scher, Linda. "Hurricanes." *Kids Discover*. June 2002: 1–20.

Seibert, Patricia. *Discovering El Nino*. Brookfield: Millbrook Press, 1999.

Our Universe Master Supply List

The following table lists all the supplies used for *God's Design for Heaven & Earth: Our Universe* activities. You will need to look up the individual lessons in the student book to obtain the specific details for the individual activities (such as quantity, color, etc.). The letter "c" denotes that the lesson number refers to the challenge activity. Common supplies such as colored pencils, construction paper, markers, scissors, tape, etc., are not listed.

Supplies needed (see lessons for details)	Lesson
☐ Aluminum foil	20, 29
☐ Aquarium or other empty glass case	22
☐ Balloons	30
☐ Basketball or volleyball	3, 14, 25
☐ Bathroom scale	27
☐ Bible	1, 18c, 35
☐ Building blocks	33
☐ Calculator	6c, 27
☐ Candle	22
☐ Cardboard	11c
☐ Cereal bowls	23
☐ Clipboard	15c
☐ Craft wire	34
☐ Cups (clear plastic or glass)	15, 19c, 21c, 22, 23c, 26
☐ Dry ice	22
☐ Flashlight	3, 4, 6, 7, 14, 15c, 16, 19c, 21c 26, 35
☐ Flour	10
☐ Food coloring	26
☐ Glitter	9
☐ Globe	21
☐ Gloves	22
☐ Golf ball	2, 10
☐ Graph paper	20c
☐ Hairdryer	19

Supplies needed (see lessons for details)	Lesson
☐ Ice	15, 19
☐ Index card	12c, 19c, 25c, 34c
☐ Liquid dish soap	22
☐ Magnet	28
☐ Magnifying glass	4, 19c
☐ Marbles	10, 23
☐ Masking tape	3, 18
☐ Matches	22
☐ Milk	21c
☐ Mirror	4, 12, 33
☐ Model rocket and launch pad (optional)	29
☐ Modeling clay	3c, 20c, 25c, 29
☐ Motorcycle helmet with face plate, or bike helmet (optional)	33
☐ Nut and bolt	33
☐ Orange (fruit)	21
☐ Paint	25, 34
☐ Pencils (wooden)	25c
☐ Ping-pong ball	2, 25
☐ Plastic lid or dish	28
☐ Plastic wrap	20
☐ Plastic zipper bag	
☐ Poster board/tagboard	9, 28, 29
☐ Prism (optional)	12
☐ Protractor	25c
☐ Reflector (like from a bicycle)	16
☐ Ruler	6, 20c
☐ Salt	10
☐ Shoebox	20, 20c
☐ Sidewalk chalk	13
☐ Star chart	5
☐ Steel BBs	28
☐ Straw	30

Supplies needed (see lessons for details)	Lesson	Supplies needed (see lessons for details)	Lesson
☐ String	11c, 20c, 26c, 30	☐ Towel	19
		☐ Toy houses, cars, etc.	10
☐ Styrofoam™ balls	9, 29, 34	☐ Tripod	3c
☐ Styrofoam™ rings	34	☐ Turntable (swivel chair, stool, etc.)	3c
☐ Tea bag	23c	☐ Washer	20c, 26c
☐ Telescope (optional)	4, 16c	☐ Waxed paper	32
☐ Tennis ball	14	☐ Winter clothes	33
☐ Thermometer	15, 20	☐ World atlas/map	21
☐ Thumb tacks	11c	☐ Yard stick/meter stick	6, 12c
☐ Tops (spinning toys)	18		

Our Universe Resource Guide

Suggested Books

Glow-In-The-Dark Nighttime Sky by Clint Hatchett—Easy-to-use star charts

Astronomy for Every Kid by Janice VanCleave—Many fun activities

The New Astronomy Book by Danny Faulkner—a wealth of knowledge on subjects such as supernovas, red shift, facts about planets and much more

Astronomy and the Bible: Questions and Answers by Donald DeYoung—Answers to 110 questions on astronomy and the universe

Our Created Moon by Don DeYoung & John Whitcomb—Answers to 63 questions about the "lesser light"

Universe by Design by Danny Faulkner—Explores and explains the historical development of the science of astronomy from a creationist view

The Stargazer's Guide to the Night Sky and *Taking Back Astronomy* by Dr. Jason Lisle— Christian apologetics for astronomy

Suggested Videos

Newton's Workshop by Moody Institute— Fun live-action videos with Christian themes

Journey to the Edge of Creation by Moody Institute—Beautiful film of universe

Creation Astronomy: Viewing the Universe Through Biblical Glasses by Dr. Jason Lisle (DVD)—Shows how the evidence of nature lines up perfectly with the clear teachings of Scripture

Created Cosmos: A Creation Museum Planetarium Show by Dr. Jason Lisle (DVD)—A visually stimulating tour of the universe underscoring its incomprehensible size and structure

Field Trip Ideas

- Creation Museum in Petersburg, Kentucky
- Observatory
- Space center or Space museum
- Planetarium
- Drive out to the country, away from city lights, to observe the night sky

Creation Science Resources

Answers Book for Kids Eight volumes by Ken Ham with Cindy Malott—Answers children's frequently asked questions

The New Answers Books 1–4 by Ken Ham and others—Answers frequently asked questions

The Amazing Story of Creation by Duane T. Gish—Gives scientific evidence for the creation story

Creation Science by Felice Gerwitz and Jill Whitlock—Unit study focusing on creation

Creation: Facts of Life by Gary Parker—Comparison of the evidence for creation and evolution

The Young Earth by John D. Morris—Lots of facts disproving old-earth ideas

Our Universe Works Cited

"About Foucault Pendulums and How They Prove the Earth Rotates!" http://www.calacademy.org/products/pendulum.

"About NASA." http://www.nasa.gov/about/highlights/index.html.

Arty Facts Space & Art Activities. Ed. Ellen Rodger. New York: Crabtree Publishing Company, 2002.

Behrens, June. *Sally Ride, Astronaut: An American First.* Chicago: Children's Press, 1984.

Bonnet, Bob, and Dan Keen. *Flight, Space & Astronomy.* New York: Sterling Publishing, 1997.

Bourgeois, Paulette. *The Sun.* Buffalo: Kids Can Press, Ltd., 1997.

Caprara, Giovanni. *Living in Space.* Milan: Firefly Books, 2000.

"Civilian Space Travel." http://www.kidsastronomy.com/civilian_space_travel.

Cole, Michael D. *Hubble Space Telescope Exploring the Universe.* Springfield: Enslow Publishers, Inc., 1999.

Cole, Michael D. *NASA Space Vehicles.* Berkley Heights: Enslow Publishers, Inc., 2000.

"Deep Impact." http:// deepimpact.umd.edu.

DeYoung, Donald. *Astronomy and the Bible.* Grand Rapids: Baker Book House, 1989.

Dickinson, Terrance. *Exploring the Night Sky.* Toronto: Camden House, 1987.

"Finding the Size of the Sun and the Moon." http://cse.ssl.berkeley.edu/AtHomeAstronomy/activity_03.html

"First Flight of SpaceShipOne Into Space." http://www.richard-seaman.com/Aircraft/AirShows/SpaceShipOne2004/.

Gifford, Clive. *The Kingfisher Facts and Records Book of Space.* New York: Kingfisher, 2001.

Hatchett, Clint. *The Glow-in-the-Dark Night Sky Book.* New York: Random House, 1988.

Henry, Jonathan. *The Astronomy Book.* Green Forest: Master Books, 2005.

Hitt, Robert, Jr. *The Sun's Family.* Danbury: Grolier Educational, 1998. Vol. 1 of *Outer Space.*

"James Webb Space Telescope." http://ngst.gsfc.nasa.gov.

Kerrod, Robin. *The Moon.* Minneapolis: Lerner Publications Co., 2000.

"Jupiter's New Red Spot." http://science.nasa.gov/headlines/y2006/02mar_red.

"Mauna Kea Telescopes." http://www.ifa.hawaii.edu/mko/telescope_table.htm.

Meyers, Robert. "Giant Telescopes Combine to Form World's Largest." http://www.space.com/scienceastronomy/astronomy.

National Aeronautics and Space Administration. *The Amazing Hubble Space Telescope.* John F. Kennedy Space Center: NASA, 1986.

"New Horizons." http://www.nasa.gov/mission_pages/newhorizons/main/.

"Prepared for the Mission: A Tribute to Rick Husband." *Homeschooling Today.* Mar/Apr 2003: 30–33.

Rau, Dana M. *Jupiter.* Minneapolis: Compass Point Books, 2002.

Rau, Dana M. *Mars.* Minneapolis: Compass Point Books, 2002.

Rau, Dana M. *Mercury.* Minneapolis: Compass Point Books, 2002.

Rau, Dana M. *Neptune.* Minneapolis: Compass Point Books, 2003.

Rau, Dana M. *Pluto.* Minneapolis: Compass Point Books, 2003.

Rau, Dana M. *Saturn.* Minneapolis: Compass Point Books, 2003.

Rau, Dana M. *Uranus.* Minneapolis: Compass Point Books, 2003.

Rau, Dana M. *Venus.* Minneapolis: Compass Point Books, 2002.

"Raymond Orteig—$25,000 Prize." http://www.charleslindbergh.com/plane/orteig.asp.

"Saturn Probe Sights Mystery Moon." http://news.bbc.co.uk/1/hi/sci/tech/3633297.stm.

Simon, Seymour. *Our Solar System.* New York: Morrow Junior Books, 1992.

"Saturn's Rings." http://saturn.jpl.nasa.gov/science/index.cfm?Pagel.

"Space Camp." http:// www.spacecamp.com.

Spangenburg, Ray, and Kit Moser. *Mercury.* New York: Franklin Watts, 2001.

Spangenburg, Ray, and Kit Moser. *Venus.* New York: Franklin Watts, 2001.

"Sunspots." http://www.exploratorium.edu/sunspots/research7.html.

VanCleave, Janice. *Astronomy for Every Kid.* New York: John Wiley & Sons, Inc., 1991.

VanCleave, Janice. *Solar System.* New York: John Wiley & Sons, 2000.

"The Vision for Space Exploration." http://www.nasa.gov/missions/solarsystem/explore_main_old.html.

Our Planet Earth Master Supply List

The following table lists all the supplies used for *God's Design for Heaven & Earth: Our Planet Earth* activities. You will need to look up the individual lessons in the student book to obtain the specific details for the individual activities (such as quantity, color, etc.). The letter "*c*" denotes that the lesson number refers to the challenge activity. Common supplies such as colored pencils, construction paper, markers, scissors, tape, etc., are not listed.

Supplies needed (see lessons for details)	Lesson
☐ Alum (look in grocery spice aisle)	10
☐ Baking soda	24
☐ Bar of soap	28
☐ Bible	35
☐ Brown sugar	10
☐ Building blocks	22
☐ Butterscotch candy	10
☐ Cardboard	33
☐ Chocolate chip cookies	17
☐ Chocolate chips	8, 8c, 25
☐ Chocolate syrup	25
☐ Colander	31c
☐ Cookie crumbs	25
☐ Cornstarch	11
☐ Craft sticks	10
☐ Dirt/soil (from your yard)	29, 30, 30c, 31, 31c
☐ Display box (optional)	34
☐ Egg carton	15c
☐ Epsom salt	13, 33
☐ Eye protection (goggles)	16
☐ Fine-mesh strainer	31c
☐ Food coloring	24
☐ Gloves	7, 7c
☐ Graham crackers	19c
☐ Gumballs	8
☐ Hammer	16

Supplies needed (see lessons for details)	Lesson
☐ Ice	6
☐ Ice cream	25
☐ Jar with lid	3, 6, 7c, 8
☐ Magnifying glass	10c, 16, 31
☐ Marshmallows (large)	6, 8
☐ Masking tape	1, 16
☐ Milk carton (empty, ½-gallon)	7
☐ Modeling clay	12, 21c, 22c, 28, 32
☐ Newspaper	7c, 21, 24, 31c
☐ Paint	11
☐ Paper cups	10, 11c, 30c, 31c, 33
☐ Peanut butter (creamy) or frosting	19c
☐ Petroleum jelly	12
☐ Plaster of Paris	11c, 12
☐ Plastic bottle (empty, 2-liter)	24
☐ Plastic zipper bag	7c, 8c, 28c
☐ Poster board/tagboard	34
☐ Potting soil	31
☐ Raw sugar	10
☐ Real chalk (made from limestone, not sidewalk chalk) or limestone rock	28
☐ Rocks and minerals guide	10c, 11c, 14c, 16, 34
☐ Rock and mineral samples	9c, 10c, 11c, 14c, 15c, 16, 34
☐ Rolling pin	23
☐ Sand	11
☐ Shaved ice (or fresh snow if available)	14
☐ Shoebox	23
☐ Soda pop (unopened can)	25c
☐ Sponges	13
☐ Steel wool without soap	28c
☐ Stopwatch	31c

Supplies needed (see lessons for details)	**Lesson**	**Supplies needed** (see lessons for details)	**Lesson**
☐ Straw	27, 28	☐ Tops (spinning toys)	18
☐ String	1, 33	☐ Towel	19
☐ Taffy or other soft candy	14	☐ Toy houses, cars, etc.	10
☐ Tennis ball	1	☐ Tripod	3c
☐ Toothpicks	8, 17	☐ Turntable (swivel chair, stool, etc.)	3c
☐ Toy boat	6	☐ Washer	20c, 26c
☐ Tracing paper	19	☐ Wax paper	32
☐ Unglazed ceramic tile	16	☐ Winter clothes	33
☐ Vinegar	24, 28	☐ World atlas/map	21
☐ Waxed paper	8, 14, 19c	☐ Yard stick/meter stick	6, 12c
☐ World atlas/map	5c, 20c, 24c		

Our Planet Earth Resource Guide

Suggested Books

Noah's Ark: A Feasibility Study by John Woodmorappe—An in-depth study that provides detailed answers to the major criticisms of Noah's Ark (semi-technical)

The Geology Book by Dr. John D. Morris—Well illustrated, this book presents an accurate view of earth's natural history

The Fossils Book by Gary Parker—Uncovers the exciting story of fossils from a biblical view

The Young Earth by Dr. John D. Morris—Shows how true science supports a young age for the earth

In the Days of Noah by Earl & Bonnie Snellenberger—This spectacular book gives a wide-eyed look into what life must have been like 5,000 years ago

The True Account of Noah's Ark by Tom Dooley and Bill Looney—Spectacular artwork depicting the Ark, its interior, and the pre-Flood and post-Flood world

Grand Canyon: Monument to Catastrophe by Steven A. Austin, PhD—Geologist Dr. Steven Austin explains from a biblical standpoint how Grand Canyon was formed

Footprints in the Ash by Drs. John Morris and Steven Austin—Lavishly illustrated "picture book" that shares the full, explosive story of Mount St. Helens

Exploring Planet Earth by John Hudson Tiner—a biblical/historical view of the planet

Suggested Videos

Awesome Science Volumes 1–10— Join young Noah Justice as he explores the Mammoth Site, Dinosaur National Monument, the Rocky Mountains, Glacier National Park, Meteor Crater and Petrified Forest, Grand Canyon, Yellowstone, Mount St. Helens, Yosemite, and the John Day Fossil Beds in these 30-minute programs

Newton's Workshop by Moody Institute—Excellent Christian science series

Wonders of God's Creation by Moody Institute—three-DVD set includes *Planet Earth*, *Animal Kingdom*, and *Human Life*; beautiful photography

The Privileged Planet—Shows why the Earth is special and could not have happened by chance. (Intelligent Design)

Mount St. Helens by Institute for Creation Research—shows many exciting discoveries

Grand Canyon Monument to the Flood by ICR—tours Grand Canyon from creation perspective

Field Trip Ideas

- Creation Museum in Petersburg, Kentucky
- Museum with geology exhibits
- Hike in the hills or mountains
- Mining museum
- Visit a cave (one that is open to the public)

Creation Science Resources

Answers Book for Kids Eight volumes by Ken Ham with others—Answers children's frequently asked questions

The New Answers Books 1–4 by Ken Ham and others—Answers frequently asked questions

The Amazing Story of Creation by Duane T. Gish—Gives scientific evidence for the creation story

Creation Science by Felice Gerwitz and Jill Whitlock—Unit study focusing on creation

Creation: Facts of Life by Gary Parker—Comparison of the evidence for creation and evolution

The Young Earth by John D. Morris—Lots of facts disproving old-earth ideas

Visit the Kids Geology section of the Answers in Genesis website at answersingenesis.org/kids/geology.

Our Planet Earth
Works Cited

Science Encyclopedia. Ed. Susan McKeever. London: DK Publishing, 1998.

Blobaum, Cindy. *Geology Rocks!* Charlotte: Williamson Publishing, 1999.

DeYoung, Donald. *Thousands...Not Billions*. Green Forest: Master Books, 2005.

Gallant, Roy A. *Dance of Continents*. New York: Benchmark Books, 2000.

Gallant, Roy A. *Geysers—When Earth Roars*. New York: Franklin Watts, 1997.

Gallant, Roy A. *Limestone Caves*. New York: Franklin Watts, 1998.

"Geology: The Active Earth." *Nature Scope*. Feb. 1988: 1–20.

Gerwitz, Felice, and Jill Whitlock. *Creation Geology*. Fort Meyers: Media Angels, 1997.

"The Geysers." http://www.geysers.com/kids.htm.

Ham, Ken, et al. *The Answers Book*. El Cajon: Master Books - Creation Science Foundation Ltd., 1990.

Harrison, David L. *Volcanoes—Nature's Incredible Fireworks*. Honesdale: Boyds Mills Press, 2002.

Mandia, Scott A. "The Little Ice Age in Europe." http://www2.sunysuffolk.edu/mandias/lia/little_ice_age.html.

Mannes, Judy. "Volcanoes." *Kids Discover*. 1999: 1–20.

"The Mineral Native Selenium." http://mineral.galleries.com/minerals/elements/selenium/selenium.htm.

"Mineralogy 4 Kids." http://www.minsocam.org/MSA/K12/K_12.html.

Morris, John D., PhD. *The Young Earth*. Colorado Springs: Master Books, Creation Life Publishers, Inc., 1994.

Mulfinger, Jr., George, M.S., and Donald E. Snyder, M.Ed. *Earth Science for Christian Schools*. 2nd ed. Greenville: Bob Jones University Press, 1995.

"Native Element." http://www.britannica.com/EBchecked/topic/405982/native-element.

"New Mt. St. Helens Sensors Will Take Its Pulse." http://community.seattletimes.nwsource.com/archive/?date=20060924&slug=sthelens24.

Oard, Michael. "Global Warming." http://www.answersingenesis.org/articles/am/v1/n2/global-warming.

Price, Sean. "Rocks." *Kids Discover*. April 2002: 1–20.

"Creation Quotes." http://www.answersingenesis.org/home/area/tools/quotes.asp.

Ricciuti, Edward, and Margaret W. Carruthers. *First Field Guide Rocks and Minerals*. New York: Scholastic Inc., 1998.

"Rock Glacier." http://geology.about.com/library/bl/images/blrockglacier.htm.

"Rock Glaciers: An Introduction with Examples from the Austrian Alps." http://www.uibk.ac.at/projects/rockglacier/rockglacier_intro.html.

Rodrigue, Dr. "Lecture : Composition of the Earth's Crust." http://www.csulb.edu/~rodrigue/geog140/lectures/crustmaterials.html.

Su, Adrienne. "Earthquakes." *Kids Discover*. 1999: 1–20.

Vail, Tom. *Grand Canyon: A Different View*. Green Forest: Master Books, 2005.

VanCleave, Janice. *A+ Projects in Earth Science*. New York: John Wiley & Sons, 1999.

VanCleave, Janice. *Earth Science for Every Kid*. New York: John Wiley & Sons, 1991.

VanRose, Susanna. *Volcano and Earthquake*. New York: Eyewitness Books, 1992.

Woolley, Alan. *Spotter's Guide to Rocks & Minerals*. London: Usborne Publishing Ltd, 2000.

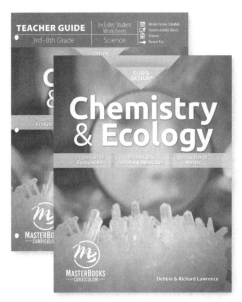